The Spirit of the Wind

Edited by
Zena Sutherland
University of Chicago

The Headway Program
Level I

Language Arts Curriculum Development Center

Open Court, La Salle, Illinois

President
M. Blouke Carus

Publisher and General Manager
Howard R. Webber

Editorial Director
Bernice Randall

Art Director
Todd Sanders

Acknowledgments

Grateful acknowledgment is given to the following publishers and copyright owners for permission granted to reprint selections from their publications. All possible care has been taken to trace ownership and secure permission for each selection included.

Atheneum Publishers, Inc. for "Footprints" from *See My Lovely Poison Ivy* by Lilian Moore, text Copyright © 1975 by Lilian Moore.

Atheneum Publishers, Inc. and Macmillan Press, Basingstoke and London, for "A Successful Halloween" adapted from *Jennifer, Hecate, Macbeth, William McKinley, and Me, Elizabeth* by E. L. Konigsburg, Copyright © 1967 by E. L. Konigsburg.

Atheneum Publishers, Inc., Macmillan Press, and McClelland and Stewart, Ltd., Toronto, for "Mouse Woman and the Tooth" from *Mouse Woman and the Mischief Makers* by Christie Harris, text Copyright © 1977 by Christie Harris.

The Bodley Head for "The Absent Present" by Norman Hunter, illustrated by Fritz Wegner, text Copyright © 1975 by Norman Hunter, illustrations © 1975 by Open Court Publishing Company.

The Headway Readers

Project Leader
Marilyn Cunningham

Advisers
Valerie Anderson
Carl Bereiter
Lawrence T. Frase
X. J. Kennedy

Design
James Buddenbaum

Editorial Assistance
John Hancock
William Maxey III
Sylvia Rosenstein

Illustration

Joanna Adamska-Koperska (81, 82, 84, 288-290), George Armstrong (60, 61, 65, 67-70), Jim Arnosky (20, 241, 354, 355, 358, 359), Lou Aronson (96, 97, 99, 100, 138, 140-142, 144), Lois Axeman (101, 103), David Beck (12, 13, 418-421), Robert Borja (36-39, 113, 114, 116, 119, 280), James Buddenbaum (322-326), Pam Carroll (202), Eva Cellini (86), Kinuko Craft (104, 105), James Cummins (21, 23, 24, 28, 30, 291, 294), David Cunningham (122, 124, 126-128, 216, 217, 219, 220, 328-330, 333, 401, 404, 407, 410), JoAnn Daley (181-185), Arless Day (282, 283, 285-287), Bert Dodson (204, 207, 213, 214), Tom Dunnington (315, 319, 393-395), Mike Eagle (145, 147, 148, 233, 234, 335, 337, 387-389), Larry Frederick (56, 57, 59, 107-110, 338, 340, 345), Hal Frenck (264, 267, 268, 383, 386-388), Pam Frost (137), Michael Hague (373, 375, 376, 378, 379), George Hamblin (17, 19), Fred Harsh (371), Dennis Hockerman (261), Bill Jacobson (187-191), Beth Leavitt (193, 194, 196, 199), Dick Martin (111, 114, 116, 119, 221, 224, 225, 227-229, 231), Robert Masheris (422, 423, 425, 427, 429, 431, 432), Charles McBarron (31, 33, 35), Carolyn McHenry (186), Tak Murakami (271, 275, 278, 279, 348-351), Gene Sharp (154-159), Dan Siculan (87-89, 93, 94, 170, 172, 175, 177, 300, 301, 304, 306, 307), Krystyna Stasiak (179, 180), Al Stine (49-51, 54, 55, 253, 255, 258, 260), Jozef Sumichrast (cover, 71), George Suyeoka (160, 161, 165, 167, 412-415, 417), George Ulrich (151-153), Jack Wallen (235-239, 296-299), David Wiesner (40, 42, 43, 45, 46), Stan Wilson (249).

Photography

Editorial Photocolor Archives (200, 201), Dan Morrill (130, 347, 391, 400), Photo Researchers, Inc./Frederick Baldwin (309-top, bottom right, bottom left), Photo Researchers, Inc./Arthur Tress (310), Photo Researchers, Inc./Languepin (317), Van Cleve Photography/ Betty Crowell (312)

Contents

Cluster 1

Cluster 2

Cluster 3

Cluster 4

Cluster 5

Cluster 6

Cluster 7

Cluster 8

The Spirit of the Wind

Cluster 1

Why Mosquitoes Buzz in People's Ears

VERNA AARDEMA

One morning a mosquito saw an iguana drinking at a water hole. The mosquito said, "Iguana, you will never believe what I saw yesterday."

"Try me," said the iguana.

The mosquito said, "I saw a farmer digging yams that were almost as big as I am."

"What's a mosquito compared to a yam?" snapped the iguana grumpily. "I would rather be deaf than listen to such nonsense!" Then he stuck two sticks in his ears and went off, mek, mek, mek, mek, through the reeds.

The iguana was still grumbling to himself when he happened to pass by a python.

The big snake raised his head and said, "Good morning, Iguana."

The iguana did not answer but lumbered on, bobbing his head, badamin, badamin.

"Now, why won't he speak to me?" said the python to himself. "Iguana must be angry about something. I'm afraid he is plotting some mischief against me!" He began looking for somewhere to hide. The first likely place he found was a rabbit hole, and in it he went, wasawusu, wasawusu, wasawusu.

When the rabbit saw the big snake coming into her burrow, she was terrified. She scurried out through her back way and bounded, kirk, kirk, kirk, across a clearing.

A crow saw the rabbit running for her life. He flew into the forest crying kaa, kaa, kaa! It was his duty to spread the alarm in case of danger.

A monkey heard the crow. He was sure that some dangerous beast was prowling near. He began screeching and leaping kili wili through the trees to help warn the other animals.

3

As the monkey was crashing through the treetops, he happened to land on a dead limb. It broke and fell on an owl's nest, killing one of the owlets.

Mother Owl was not at home. For though she usually hunted only in the night, this morning she was still out searching for one more tidbit to satisfy her hungry babies. When she returned to the nest, she found one of them dead. Her other children told her that the monkey had killed it. All that day and all that night, she sat in her tree—so sad, so sad, so sad!

Now it was Mother Owl who woke the sun each day so that the dawn could come. But this time, when she should have hooted for the sun, she did not do it.

The night grew longer and longer. The animals of the forest knew it was lasting much too long. They feared that the sun would never come back.

At last King Lion called a meeting of the animals. They came and sat down around a council fire. Mother Owl did not come, so the antelope was sent to fetch her.

When she arrived, King Lion asked, "Mother Owl, why have you not called the sun? The night has lasted long, long, long, and everyone is worried."

Mother Owl said, "Monkey killed one of my owlets. Because of that, I cannot bear to wake the sun."

The king said to the gathered animals:
"Did you hear?
It was the monkey
who killed the owlet—
and now Mother Owl won't wake the sun
so that the day can come."

4

Then King Lion called the monkey, who came before him nervously glancing from side to side.

"Monkey," said the king, "why did you kill one of Mother Owl's babies?"

"Oh, King," said the monkey, "it was the crow's fault. He was calling and calling to warn us of danger. And I went leaping through the trees to help. A limb broke under me, and it fell on the owl's nest."

The king said to the council:

"So, it was the crow
who alarmed the monkey,
who killed the owlet—
and now Mother Owl won't wake the sun
so that the day can come."

Then the king called for the crow. That big bird came flapping up. He said, "King Lion, it was the rabbit's fault! I saw her running for her life in the daytime. Wasn't that reason enough to spread an alarm?"

The king nodded his head and said to the council:

"So, it was the rabbit
who startled the crow,
who alarmed the monkey,
who killed the owlet—
and now Mother Owl won't wake the sun
so that the day can come."

Then King Lion called the rabbit. The timid little creature stood before him, one trembling paw drawn up uncertainly.

"Rabbit," cried the king, "why did you break a law of nature and go running, running, running, in the daytime?"

"Oh, King," said the rabbit, "it was the python's fault. I was in my house minding my own business when that big snake came in and chased me out."

The king said to the council:

"So, it was the python
   who scared the rabbit,
   who startled the crow,
   who alarmed the monkey,
   who killed the owlet—
   and now Mother Owl won't wake the sun
   so that the day can come."

King Lion called the python, who came slithering, wasawusu, wasawusu, past the other animals. "But, King," he cried, "it was the iguana's fault! He wouldn't speak to me. And I thought he was plotting some mischief against me. When I crawled into the rabbit's hole, I was only trying to hide."

The king said to the council:

"So, it was the iguana
   who frightened the python,
   who scared the rabbit,
   who startled the crow,
   who alarmed the monkey,
   who killed the owlet—
   and now Mother Owl won't wake the sun
   so that the day can come."

Now the iguana was not at the meeting. For he had not heard the summons. The antelope was sent to fetch him.

All the animals laughed when they saw the iguana coming, badamin, badamin, with the sticks still stuck in his ears.

7

King Lion pulled out the sticks. Then he asked, "Iguana, what evil have you been plotting against the python?"

"None! None at all!" cried the iguana. "Python is my friend!"

"Then why wouldn't you say good morning to me?" demanded the snake.

"I didn't hear you or even see you!" said the iguana. "Mosquito told me such a big lie, I couldn't bear to listen to it. So I put sticks in my ears."

"So that's why you had sticks in your ears!" laughed the lion.

"Yes," said the iguana. "It was the mosquito's fault."

King Lion said to the council:
"So, it was the mosquito
    who annoyed the iguana,
    who frightened the python,
    who scared the rabbit,
    who startled the crow,
    who alarmed the monkey,
    who killed the owlet—
    and now Mother Owl won't wake the sun
    so that the day can come."

9

"Punish the mosquito! Punish the mosquito!" cried all the animals.

When Mother Owl heard that, she was satisfied. She turned her head toward the east and hooted, "Hoo! Hooooo! Hooooooo!"

And the sun came up.

Meanwhile, the mosquito had listened to it all from a nearby bush. She crept under a curly leaf and was never found and brought before the council.

But because of this the mosquito has a guilty conscience. To this day she goes about whining in people's ears, "Zeee! Is everyone still angry at me?"

When she does that, she gets an honest answer.

KPAO!

10

11

What Is a UFO?

LARRY A. CIUPIK

One sunny afternoon a few years ago, Tonia and Tina Hays were chasing one another down their driveway, playing tag. Suddenly something strange appeared over the pond in the field near their home. It looked like a large balloon and seemed only a few hundred yards away.

"Look!" Tonia shouted excitedly.

"It's moving!" exclaimed Tina.

The twins pointed out the blue-gray object to their younger brother, but he was too busy playing to be interested. Then they ran into the house to tell their mother.

"Mommy! Mommy!" they called together. "There's a funny balloon out by the pond."

Their mother tried to calm them as they pulled her out the garage door toward the field. At first Mrs. Hays thought the object was a large hot-air balloon or a blimp. But, oddly, it was gradually changing color from blue-gray to red. Then it began to rise. It went higher and higher till an amazing thing happened—it vanished! It was not simply hidden by the clouds; it disappeared suddenly and completely, as if a grand magician had said some magic words.

That night the Hays's next-door neighbor saw something strange in the same field near the pond. Next to the usual dim glow of the power-line-tower lights she saw a new red light so bright it made her eyes water. She wanted to run and tell someone about it, but before she was able to move very far, the light rose and disappeared.

12

It was the first time these people had ever seen a UFO.

What is a UFO? It is an Unidentified Flying Object. Thousands of people have seen things in the sky that they could not identify. Many of these things *can* be identified, however, by astronomers and other scientists. Such objects are called IFOs, or Identified Flying Objects. True UFOs are those flying objects that even scientists cannot identify or explain. Of every five UFOs reported, one remains unexplained.

During the past twenty-five years, UFOs have been studied by the U.S. Air Force, by other government agencies and committees, and by interested people throughout the world. In 1974 several leading investigators in the United States organized a Center for UFO Studies to collect and study reports of UFOs, which numbered nearly 500 in 1974 alone. Perhaps groups like these will be able to solve the mysteries of UFO sightings.

One interesting sighting occurred on July 9, 1974. At about one o'clock in the morning, two police officers in Kingston, New York, saw an object hovering over a park. It was thirty feet long and football-shaped. It had some lights that flickered on and off and other lights that glowed steadily. When the UFO slowly approached to within fifty feet of the police car, one officer shined a spotlight on it. When he turned off the spotlight, a light from the UFO lit up the entire car! Then the UFO moved out of sight without any sound of an engine or motor. The officers tried to follow the object, but could not sight it again.

Other people, short distances away from the park, reported seeing the same kind of object in the sky at about the same time that night.

Dr. J. Allen Hynek, director of the Center for UFO Studies, has divided unexplained UFO sightings into two groups. The first group is called distant encounters and includes reports of daytime disks, night lights, and radar sightings.

The second group, called close encounters, includes three types of close-up sightings. "Close encounters of the first kind" are sightings with no effects. "Close encounters of the second kind" are those with noticeable effects. A sighting with occupants reported is a "close encounter of the third kind." The police sighting in New York, for example, would be a close encounter of the first kind.

You may have seen movies about creatures from outer space invading earth. Or you may have read about journeys we earthlings might make with our "starships" hundreds of years from now. But did you know that during the past twenty-five years over 900 UFO reports have mentioned sightings of unusual beings? These are not reports of monsters, but of humanlike creatures called humanoids. The reports have come from people around the world, people who have no reason to lie about what they saw.

UFO investigators cannot dismiss these 900 cases just because they are very strange. In fact, many other UFO cases are just as strange but in different ways. For example, Air Force jets have frequently chased UFOs, but have never caught one. Some UFOs waited till the jets were after them and then put on a burst of speed or made a sharp turn and disappeared.

The actions of UFOs and the sightings of humanoids have led some investigators to think that UFOs must come from other planets. However, biologists say there is very little chance that intelligent creatures from other worlds would look like us. Because of the great number of elements in the universe and the many different kinds of stars, it is highly unlikely that outer-space beings would develop in the same way we have. The most important argument against visitors from other planets, though, is the tremendous number of sightings. You see, even the *nearest* star system, Alpha Centauri, is 25,000,000,000,000 (25 trillion) miles away. Even with our fastest rockets it would take thousands of years to get there! But what if they have faster rockets, you might ask. The fastest possible speed is the speed of light—186,000 miles per second—and even a light from that "nearby" star system would take more than four years to reach earth. To account for all of the sightings in the United States alone (assuming everyone who sees a UFO reports it), outer-space beings would have to launch several thousand spaceships every year!

If the sightings are not caused by visitors from other planets, what are they caused by? Some UFO experts have suggested time travel. Other experts simply say they do not know the cause of UFOs. They need more time and information to find out the truth. And they need your help. If you ever see an Unidentified Flying Object, write to: The Center for UFO Studies, P.O. Box 11, Northfield, Illinois 60093. Include your name, address, age, and everything you can think of about the object: its color, shape, date and time seen, and so forth.

With everyone's help in reporting sightings of UFOs, we might be able to answer one of the most puzzling questions ever asked—what is a UFO?

Amelia Earhart's Last Flight

GILBERT GRAIL

Early on the morning of June 1, 1937, Amelia Earhart and her navigator, Fred Noonan, took off from Miami, Florida, to fly around the world at the equator. The 28,000-mile flight would be a "first" in aviation history.

Amelia Earhart already had several "firsts" in the history books. In 1928 she had become the first woman passenger to fly the Atlantic. Four years later she had been the first woman pilot to fly the Atlantic alone. In 1935 she had made the first solo flight from Hawaii to California. Later that same year she had accomplished the first nonstop solo flight from Mexico City to New York.

As she piloted her small plane out over the Atlantic on this sunny June morning, she must have felt again the excitement of starting something new and daring. It was to be her last long-distance flight, she had told reporters.

Amelia Earhart was born in Atchison, Kansas, in 1898. In the early 1920s she had become interested in flying. To earn money for flying lessons, she had worked in an office, driven a truck, operated a photography studio, and been a social worker. The 1928 transatlantic flight had made her world-famous.

Now, nine years later, people all over the world were following her final daring journey with excited interest. The trip had been carefully planned and would include landings at twenty-four places scattered around the globe. The first stop was in Puerto Rico and AE (as she liked to call herself) landed there on the afternoon of June 1.

The next morning the two travelers flew across the Caribbean Sea, south to Venezuela. There they landed at a small town on the edge of the jungle and the next day were off to Paramaribo in the Dutch colony of

Guiana. Then they headed south again, to cross the equator for the first time and eventually reach the city of Natal on the coast of Brazil.

All had gone well on these relatively short flights. But now came the first real test: to cross the Atlantic Ocean from Natal to the African city of Dakar. It was a distance of 1900 miles. AE and Noonan took off before daybreak on June 7 and were over the coast of Africa thirteen hours later. They missed Dakar but landed at another Senegalese city. Then began their short hops over the jungles and deserts of north central Africa. Without accurate maps, Noonan often had a difficult time determining where they were. They landed at seven remote places. The seventh was Assab on the Red Sea coast of Ethiopia. From there they made the long flight to the city of Karachi in India. It was now June 16.

As the two aviators flew from Karachi to Calcutta, the heavy rains of the monsoons buffeted their tiny plane. These rains were to be a problem until the fliers reached Bangkok in Siam. There the weather improved. The 900-mile flight from Bangkok to Singapore went smoothly.

After flying over the East Indies, the fliers landed at Port Darwin on Australia's northern coast on June 29. To reduce weight on the plane, they left their parachutes at Port Darwin. The rest of the journey would be over the Pacific Ocean and the parachutes would be of no use.

Earhart and Noonan reached Lae on the island of New Guinea the next day. They had been traveling for thirty days and had flown 22,000 miles. Their next destination was Howland Island, a tiny island in the vast Pacific, more than 2500 miles away.

Howland Island was to be the first American territory the travelers had encountered since leaving Puerto Rico. A U. S. Coast Guard ship, the *Itasca*, was at Howland waiting to help them locate the island by radio. AE's plane took off from Lae at ten o'clock on the morning of July 2.

On the *Itasca* tense hours passed as the crew tried and failed to establish radio contact with the plane. Finally, at 2:45 A.M. on July 3, AE's voice came through, badly hampered by static. All the radio operators could make out were three words, "cloudy and overcast."

It was obvious that the plane was not receiving the ship's repeated messages. An hour later AE's voice again was heard asking the *Itasca* to contact her.

Still unable to establish contact, the radio operators next heard from Earhart at 6:15 A.M., saying she thought the plane was about two hundred miles from Howland. A half-hour later she reported, "about one hundred miles out." Further messages were received at 7:42 and 7:58, reporting "gas is running low," and "cannot hear you." At 8:00, she reported at last that she was receiving the *Itasca*'s signal. Then there was silence for the next forty-five minutes.

At 8:45 A.M., AE's voice came in loud and clear. "We are running north and south," she said and gave their exact compass heading. These were the last words heard from her.

The *Itasca* continued trying to reach her for several hours. Navy ships searched the area for more than two weeks. But Amelia Earhart and Fred Noonan had vanished.

In the years that have passed since then, many people have tried to find out what happened to the brave fliers. Many theories have been suggested, but none has been proved. Their fate is still a mystery.

19

Footprints

It was snowing
Last night,
And today
I can see who came
This way.

A dog ran lightly here,
And a cat.
A rabbit hopped by and—
What was THAT?

A twelve-toed foot
Two yards wide?
Another step here
In just one stride?

It was snowing
Last night.
Who came past?
I'll never be knowing
For I am going
The OTHER way,
Fast.

—Lilian Moore

20

Settling In

LOUISA R. SHOTWELL

Roosevelt Grady and his family are crop-pickers and are always on the move, going wherever the crops are ready for picking. Now they are on their way to a new camp with Cap, their crew leader, to pick beans.

One day as they were going north, Cap Jackson let Roosevelt and Matthew and Sister ride alongside of him right up in the front of the truck. They begged him to tell them about Willowbrook.

"Willowbrook? It's a whale of a camp," he told them. "Room for half a dozen crews like ours. Maybe more. Must be twenty cabins all hitched together in a single row. And they have three rows like that. Fill up three sides of a square, they do. A great big hollow square, one row of cabins to each side. Right in the middle of the square there's a shack with cookstoves in it for folks that don't bring along their own stoves the way your mamma does. The cookshack has a juke box in it, too, and a loudspeaker, so I can call my folks to come when it's time to cash in their bean tickets."

Roosevelt knew what that meant. So did Sister and Matthew. When you've picked your hamperful of beans, you drag it off to be weighed, and then you get a ticket. Later on Papa trades in the ticket for money. Fifty cents, seventy-five cents, something like that, depending on how big the hamper is and what they are paying that day. Florida hampers weigh thirty-two pounds, sometimes, when they're full.

"How'll I know which cabin's ours?" asked Matthew. "If they're hitched together and they all look alike, how'll I know when I'm home?"

"You'll get to know. Each cabin has its own door with a number on it to tell you which one your family belongs in. Has its own window too."

"A square has four sides. You told us about three of them. What's on the fourth side of the square?" Roosevelt wanted to know. "The empty side?"

"Guess," Cap ordered.

"Willowbrook. A brook. I guess a brook. With fish in it." That was Matthew.

"Wrong," said Cap.

"I guess a willow tree," said Sister. "Nice and droopy with lots of shade to play in."

"Wrong."

"A schoolhouse?" asked Roosevelt. He was quite sure this was not the right answer. He was only hoping.

"All wrong," said Cap. "No brook, and I don't recall seeing a willow tree anywhere around. The name of that camp's a fake. No school either. There's a big brick school building five miles down the road for the resident children, but there isn't any school at Willowbrook."

"Then what does fill up the empty side of the hollow square?" asked Matthew. "Tell us, Cap. We give up."

"Beans," said Cap. "A bean field, right on the doorstep."

When they finally came to Willowbrook, sure enough there was the hollow square with the cookshack in the middle and on the square's empty side, the bean field. No brook. No willow tree. No schoolhouse.

23

The way it worked at Willowbrook, your papa stood in line at the cookshack door and waited his turn for a man called Bucky to say which cabin his family could have. Bucky was the camp manager. His entire name was Bucky Bean, and he ran things at Willowbrook.

"Bucky Bean?" With his index finger Matthew scoured out his right ear and then his left, making believe he hadn't heard right. "Is his name really and truly Bean? Mr. Bucky Bean?"

"Must be," Mamma answered. "That's what your papa said, and I don't know why he'd make it up."

"Ho—ho—ho," said Matthew. "Mr. Bean's in charge of beans." He thumped on his chest with his fists and limped around in a circle, chanting:

> Mister Bean
> What I mean
> Pick 'em clean
> Or ol' man Bean
> He'll get himself
> A bean machine!

"Matthew!" Mamma spoke sharp. "Where'd you hear that?"

"No place. It just popped out of my mouth. Don't you like it? I do. Do you want some more? Bean—seen—green—queen—screen—"

Just then Papa came back from standing in line. "Number Seven," he announced. "That's where we belong. See who can find it first."

On each cabin door there was painted in black a huge sprawly number. It should have been easy to find Cabin Number Seven, but it wasn't. There was something queer about those numbers.

Sister was the first to spot Number Seven, and while Roosevelt was still puzzling in his head, she figured out what was the matter. Times were when Sister promised to grow up as smart as Mamma, and this was one of those times.

"There's ours," she cried, and she darted over to a door and pointed.

"That's no seven," said Roosevelt. He was tired and cross, and he guessed he knew what a seven ought to look like.

"Maybe it's not a seven," said Sister, "but the man who painted it thought it was. Look." And pointing, she counted out the cabins backwards to the beginning of the row, "Seven, Six, Five, Four, Three, Two, One. This one's Number Seven, all right."

The figures looked like this:

ɭƐϨϷƐϨ↾

"That old Camp Manager Bucky Bean must have let a first grader do his painting for him," said Roosevelt, crosser than ever because he hadn't located Number Seven ahead of Sister.

"Maybe," said Sister. "But whoever did it, he looks at things through a looking glass. Backwards!" She giggled, and so did everybody else, even Roosevelt. Once you knew what was the matter, the figures did look comical.

Roosevelt lugged his mother's metal suitcase into Cabin Number Seven and set it in the middle of the floor. Then he ran back outdoors to have a look around the camp. He walked along, counting cabins. Starting from the bean field, the three sides of the hollow square had twenty cabins to a side. Just what Cap said. Times three, that made sixty families. Suppose every family was like the Gradys and had six people to it; there could be six times sixty people living in that camp. Six times sixty—360 folks. Could mean as many as seven or eight crews, nine or ten, even. Not that many now because the whole far side of the square stood padlocked and empty.

But just suppose. Suppose you had ten crew leaders and each one picked out crews as different from each other as Cap Jackson and Digger Burton did. And suppose half the crew leaders didn't like the other half any better than Cap liked Digger. There'd sure enough be plenty of chance for quarrelings.

Cabin Number Eight had a fat lady living in it named Mrs. Clay. She was big enough to fill up the cabin with no help from anybody else, but besides herself there were her husband James, skinny and sour looking, and a large collection of children, all girls.

The Gradys hadn't been one hour at Willowbrook before they found themselves acquainted with Pearly Ann Clay. Pearly Ann was seven years old and so was Sister, and right away they started being girlfriends. But nobody in the Grady family had the rest of the Clays sorted out until Matthew met Mrs. Clay.

It was the next day. Mrs. Clay had just finished her wash and was hanging out her clothes on a line stretched from her cabin to the cookshack roof. Her clothespins were in a bucket on the ground. She would put half a dozen of the pins in her mouth at once and pull them out one at a time as she needed them. She had a wide mouth to suit the rest of her. It accommodated six clothespins without stretching.

Mrs. Clay hadn't noticed Matthew at all, and when he said to her, "Mrs. Clay, how many children have you got?" she was so startled she blew the clothespins right out of her mouth. They flew every which way. Matthew limped around picking them up and when he brought them back, he said, "How about if I hand these to you one at a time out of the bucket? That way we can have a satisfactory conversation."

Mrs. Clay gave Matthew a rather peculiar look, but she said, "Let's try." Matthew handed her a clothespin. "Now then. What did you ask me?"

"How many children have you got?"

"Well, let me see," said Mrs. Clay. "We'll start at the top. Two clothespins this time, please. There." She set the two pins firmly into a pair of blue jeans. "That's Marlene and Cherry. Twins."

Matthew handed her another pin.

"This is Lulubelle. Now two more, please. These are

27

Sue Ellen and Tillie. Twins again." Now it was diapers she was hanging up. She reached down her hand to Matthew for another pin. "And one for little Baby Bethalene. Six girls, and they're all mine.

"Now one for Wanda. She's the child of Clay's brother, and she's the size of my Marlene and Cherry.

Wanda scraps with her own folks so she mostly travels with us. That's seven."

"And Pearly Ann," said Matthew, handing up another clothespin.

"And Pearly Ann," said Mrs. Clay. "She makes eight. Eight girls. That's how many children I've got."

"Where'd Pearly Ann come from?" persisted Matthew.

"Pearly Ann?" Mrs. Clay hung up the last dress from her basket. Thin blue-and-white stripes it had, and she kind of smoothed it out with her hands as she talked. "When Pearly Ann was a mite of a baby, no longer than a shoe box, her mamma died. Down in South Carolina, in the strawberries, it was. Her papa, he was half crazy, he felt so bad to lose his wife. And he said to me, 'What am I going to do with Pearly Ann?' So I said, 'You give Pearly Ann to me and don't you fret. I'll look after her just as easy, right along with mine. One extra isn't going to be a speck more bother than what I've got already.' And that's the way it's been. Seven years now and Pearly Ann fits in with us so good, I declare I mostly disremember she didn't start out being my baby at all."

When Matthew felt like working his memory, there was nothing he couldn't recall. That night the Gradys heard every word of his talk with Mrs. Clay, exactly the way it happened.

The thought of those clothespins tickled Papa so hard he choked. He had to wipe his eyes before he could speak one word.

"There's one thing about you, Matthew," he said.

"What's one thing about me?" asked Matthew.

Papa picked him up and set him on his knee. Very gently he rubbed his feet, the good one and the lame one.

Then he put a finger under Matthew's chin and tipped up his face.

"There's nothing wrong with your head," Papa told him. "Or your funny bone."

Mamma was struck to know about all those Clay children. "Think of that," said Mamma. "Six girls of her own and two more that don't rightly belong to her, but she keeps them in the family just as if they did. And that poor South Carolina strawberry-picker who lost his wife, her telling him one more child wouldn't be a speck of bother. What's more, I do believe she meant it. I declare, I'm going to talk to that woman. Find out how she does it. I marvel at her."

"You have anything in mind?" asked Papa, in his teasing voice. Before Mamma could answer he went to speaking serious. "Addie Grady, I do say this, and I want you to hearken to it. You have no call to marvel at any other woman. How ever many extra children she adds on to her family, she can't beat you. You're the best."

"Henry Grady," said Mamma, tossing her head. "How you talk." But she did look pleased.

The Lost Colony

DAN LACY

Roanoke Island is small, flat, and sandy. It is about twelve miles long and three miles wide. It lies off the coast of North Carolina, hidden from the Atlantic Ocean by a long chain of narrow islands known as the Outer Banks. Even today only very small ships can reach the island, and then only by threading their way through narrow inlets in the Outer Banks.

In the summer of 1587 a small band of men, women, and children landed on Roanoke Island and began to clear the trees and to build huts. They had sailed from England in three tiny ships, a journey that had lasted for weeks. They came with food and tools and supplies to build homes and to establish a permanent colony in the New World.

Since Columbus had landed in America nearly a century before, the Spanish had settled Florida, Mexico, parts of South America, and most of the larger islands in the Caribbean. Fortunes were made for Spain from the gold and silver mines in Mexico and Peru. An ocean current called the Gulf Stream flows northward from Florida to North Carolina along the coast of what is now the United States. Every year fleets of large, slow Spanish ships, laden with American treasure for the king of Spain, made their way along this coast, following the Gulf Stream until they could strike out east across the Atlantic.

England was then a relatively poor country, far less powerful than Spain. But the English were eager to share in the treasures of the New World. They wanted an English empire in America. They also wanted a chance to capture Spanish ships and seize their cargoes of gold and silver.

Roanoke Island gave them a chance to do both. It would be their first colony on the new continent. And light, swift English ships could slip out through the inlets and capture Spanish treasure ships. The large Spanish warships could not follow them back through the inlets.

Sir Walter Raleigh, a wealthy English knight, was given the right to explore and settle the coast of what is now the southern United States. In 1584 explorers sent by Raleigh picked Roanoke Island as the best place for a first colony. The following year a large group of soldiers was sent to the island to build a fort. They used up all their supplies, and before a relief ship came they abandoned the fort and returned to England.

When the English settlers landed in 1587, they expected to find more than a dozen men who had been left to hold the island over the winter of 1586–87. But all they found was one skeleton and the ruins of a fort. From friendly Indians they learned that a band of hostile Indians had attacked the fort and killed most of the men. The rest had fled in a boat and disappeared.

In spite of this warning of the dangers around them, the colonists set out to make their new homes. The fort was rebuilt. Dirt-floored huts were erected. A wall of tree trunks sunk deep in the ground was built around the little settlement. Fields were cleared for crops. The colonists knew, however, that they did not have enough supplies to last them until crops were harvested the following year. They urged John White, their governor, to return to England and send ships immediately with more supplies.

33

Before White left at the end of August 1587, the first children of English parents were born in America. Two of the settlers were Governor White's daughter, Eleanor, and her husband, Ananias Dare. On August 18 their baby was born, a little girl named Virginia. Before a week passed a second baby was born, a boy to Dyonis and Margery Harvey.

White sailed from a hopeful colony. But when he reached England, he found the country preparing for war with Spain. It was too dangerous for ships to sail the stormy Atlantic that winter, and with the arrival of spring 1588 England thought only about defending itself against the huge Spanish fleet that was ready to invade. No ships or sailors could be spared for any other purpose. The great battle with the Spanish fleet took place in the summer of 1588. Helped by a violent storm, the English won a complete victory. But Sir Walter Raleigh had no money left for relief ships for Roanoke that year. In 1589 a relief ship was sent, but it was turned back by storms and a Spanish attack.

Not until 1590 did John White get back to Roanoke Island. When he reached the wall around the little village, his heart sank. The gate hung open, and on one of the gateposts were carved the letters C R O. Inside all was abandoned. The huts stood empty. Pumpkins grew on the dirt floors and vines twined through the windows. The only sound came from deer scampering away. A trench had been dug, in which trunks and boxes had been buried. Books, papers, and pieces of armor were scattered about. The settlers were gone, leaving nothing except the buried chests and a few bars of iron and lead too heavy to carry.

They were gone, but where? On a tree was carved the word CROATOAN. When he left, White had agreed with the colonists that if they moved, they would carve on a tree the name of the place to which they were going. If they were in serious trouble, they were to carve a cross above the name. There was no cross, and White was cheered by this. He knew of a friendly Indian village nearby called Croatan. A chief from the village, Manteo, had

returned to England with some of the earlier explorers. He spoke English and had been very helpful to White's colonists. No doubt the colonists had gone to his village when they ran short of food or were threatened by other Indians. At least there was no evidence of fighting on Roanoke Island.

White hoped to leave the next day for Croatan. But a severe storm that night left his ships battered and unable to sail. The captain of the little fleet had to put out to sea and he would not bring his damaged ships back to the stormy Outer Banks. John White never got back to Roanoke, and no white person ever saw the settlers again. They became the Lost Colony.

Even today, nobody knows what happened to them. It seems that they stayed at Roanoke Island for a year or two and then left, but not because of an Indian attack. They probably ran out of food and went to Croatan, hoping to live on fish and such food as they could get from Manteo's friendly tribe. They may have built a ship or used a small boat left with them and tried to return to England and been lost at sea.

Twenty years later the English settled at Jamestown, in Virginia, and sent out explorers to learn the fate of the lost colonists. They heard many rumors; most of them said that Powhatan, the Indian ruler of the whole area, had wiped out the colony because it had become friendly with tribes that warred with him. Other rumors said that some of the settlers had survived and lived among the Indians. But no such survivors, if there were any, were ever found. Whatever their fate, they are remembered as the first English people who tried to make their homes and their children's homes forever in the New World.

The Riddle

I gave my love a cherry that has no stone.
I gave my love a chicken that has no bone.
I gave my love a ring that has no end.
I gave my love a baby with no cryin'.

Can there be a cherry that has no stone?
Can there be a chicken that has no bone?
Can there be a ring that has no end?
Can there be a baby with no cryin'?

A cherry when it's bloomin' it has no stone.
A chicken in an eggshell it has no bone.
A ring when it is rollin' it has no end.
A baby when it's sleepin' has no cryin'.

— American Folk Song

36

Lucy Gray; or, Solitude

Oft I had heard of Lucy Gray:
And, when I crossed the wild,
I chanced to see at break of day
The solitary child.

No mate, no comrade Lucy knew;
She dwelt on a wide moor,
—The sweetest thing that ever grew
Beside a human door!

You yet may spy the fawn at play,
The hare upon the green;
But the sweet face of Lucy Gray
Will never more be seen.

"To-night will be a stormy night—
You to the town must go;
And take a lantern, Child, to light
Your mother through the snow."

"That, Father! will I gladly do:
'Tis scarcely afternoon—
The minster-clock has just struck two,
And yonder is the moon!"

The storm came on before its time:
She wandered up and down;
And many a hill did Lucy climb:
But never reached the town.

The wretched parents all that night
Went shouting far and wide;
But there was neither sound nor sight
To serve them for a guide.

At day-break on a hill they stood
That overlooked the moor;
And thence they saw the bridge of wood,
A furlong from their door.

They wept—and, turning homeward, cried,
"In heaven we all shall meet";
—When in the snow the mother spied
38 The print of Lucy's feet.

Then downwards from the steep hill's edge
They tracked the footmarks small;
And through the broken hawthorn hedge,
And by the long stone-wall.

And then an open field they crossed:
The marks were still the same;
They tracked them on, nor ever lost;
And to the bridge they came.

They followed from the snowy bank
Those footmarks, one by one,
Into the middle of the plank;
And further there were none!

—Yet some maintain that to this day
She is a living child;
That you may see sweet Lucy Gray
Upon the lonesome wild.

O'er rough and smooth she trips along,
And never looks behind;
And sings a solitary song
That whistles in the wind.

—William Wordsworth

Basil and the Case of the Counterfeit Cheese

EVE TITUS

Who has not heard of Sherlock Holmes? People hail him as the master detective of all time.

Mice proudly hail their own super sleuth, Basil of Baker Street. No case is too difficult or too dangerous for this daring detective, and criminals cringe at the sound of his name.

I am Dr. David Q. Dawson, and Basil and I lodge at Baker Street, Number 221 B, which is also the address of Mr. Sherlock Holmes and Dr. John H. Watson. The men dwell abovestairs and the mice belowstairs, in the cellar community of Holmestead, so named by Basil.

My friend learns his detective lore by listening at Sherlock Holmes's feet when scientific sleuthing is discussed. He takes many notes in shortpaw, hidden behind a chair leg.

To give you an example of my friend's genius, I shall describe how he solved a case in a few short hours, a case that had baffled Mouseland Yard detectives for weeks.

On a crisp October morning in the year 1894, Mrs. Judson served our breakfast. We were to sail at midnight on a secret mission to Mexico.

Basil had a second helping of cheese soufflé while he scanned the *Mouse Times*. "Dawson, the Case of the Counterfeit Cheese is still unsolved! Hundreds of mice with broken teeth crowd into dentists' waiting rooms. The fake cheeses look and smell like real cheeses. Mice sniff them in dark passageways and gnaw away. Their reward? The ghastly sound of breaking teeth! There are no clues. Policemice remove the counterfeits, but others appear. Do you recall the case in which a golden hill of cheese concealed a deadly mousetrap?"

I shuddered. "That evil device was invented by Professor Ratigan, leader of London's mouse underworld and your sworn enemy. Is this another of his schemes? However, it seems to me that only dentists would profit. I saw my dentist last week. Dr. Tuchman's office was jammed! I joked, told him he'd make millions, but he didn't even smile, and his paws kept twitching and trembling. He's usually a jolly sort."

"Hmmm. Mrs. Judson, what of your dentist?"

"Mr. Basil, mine wasn't happy about the crowds of patients, either. And, if you'll excuse the expression, he was as nervous as a cat!"

My friend looked thoughtful. "My own dentist, Dr. Richardson, is the happy-go-lucky type, but yesterday he was as jumpy as a kangaroo. His paws shook so much that I feared he'd fill the wrong tooth! One nervous dentist might be a coincidence, but—*three*? There must be a reason!" He leaped up. "By Jove! Can it be that—"

There was a knock at the door. Mrs. Judson admitted Inspector Hollyer, of the Yard. "Basil, we need your help! Superintendent Bigelow asks you to solve the Case of the Counterfeit Cheese."

41

"The case interests me. I'll do my best to solve it by dark and still make that midnight sailing to Mexico. Tell me all you know, Inspector."

We settled back in our chairs, prepared to hear the latest information on the case. However, Hollyer had nothing new to report, except that Mouseland Yard detectives had questioned every mouse dentist in London, thirty-two in number.

"They were all nervous," he told us. "We decided this was due to long hours of overwork, fixing broken teeth far into the night."

"Overwork? Stuff and nonsense!" cried Basil. "There's more to it than that. Dawson, kindly pass me the London Mouse Dental Directory."

I fetched the volume from the shelf, and he skimmed the pages, mumbling to himself. "Hmmm. Richardson, Stanley. Schooling: Spring View, Brierley Preparatory, Rodental College. Married Simone Vernet, son Alex at Brierley. Tuchman, Bernard. Same schools, son Adam at Brierley. St. Clair, N., Trevor, V., Windibank, J. Hmmm. All have sons at Brierley."

He snapped the book shut. "Hollyer, tell Superintendent Bigelow that I have a clue in the Counterfeit Cheese Case. It's important that I see my dentist at once. Come along, Dawson!"

We saw Dr. Richardson in his private office.

Basil wasted no words. "You are being terrorized, and I know why. In heaven's name, speak!"

Richardson hung his head. "Alas, I dare not!"

At that moment his wife entered, crying, "*Cheri, cheri*! Is there any news of our son?"

"Simone, say no more!" warned the dentist.

Turning, she saw Basil, and her eyes lit up.

"M'sieu Basil, you are our one hope! Only you can outwit the evil Professor Ratigan. I'll stay silent no longer, but will reveal everything. Only the sons of London mouse dentists are accepted at Brierley School. Every October the school closes, and the students and a guide go off on a camping and cycling tour. They write home each day, but this year four days passed with no mail. The lads start by riding through the mouse town of Brierley Glen. The Mayor told us they hadn't been seen! Worried, we parents decided to tell the police the next day. And then—" She trembled. "That very night Stanley and I awoke to see the Professor at our bedside. He boasted, 'I invented the fake cheeses, so the money for fixing broken teeth belongs to me. My gangs will collect from now on. Tell the police, or that busybody, Basil of Baker Street, and you'll never see your sons again!' Then he was gone! Gangsters come daily to collect. When dentists ask about their children, the scoundrels sneer. Please help us!"

Basil patted her paw. "Madame, do not despair! They shall be saved! We must leave you now."

44

We rushed along the London streets. At Charing Cross Station Basil stole aboard a people's train for Chatham. From there he planned to hike to the mouse town of Brierley Glen.

I went home. Basil returned at nine that night, just before Hollyer arrived, happily excited.

"Superintendent Bigelow thanks you, sir! After you telephoned the location of the counterfeit cheese factory, we raided it and made some arrests, but Ratigan and his chief aides escaped. However, we closed down the factory."

"Good work!" said Basil. "Bigelow, wise as a judge, is bound to promote you. Now I'll tell you my part in the affair. In Brierley Glen I rented a bicycle and rode to Brierley School. Not a soul was in sight—I was the solitary cyclist. The buildings were set back from the road, except for the bicycle shed, just inside the front gates. I squeezed under and entered the shed. The bicycles were grimy and dusty, tumbled together in wild disorder, and tossed every which way. I'd found my final clue!"

"Enlighten us," begged Hollyer. "What clue?"

"Elementary, my dear mice! Boys, be they mouse or human, may neglect their clothes, their rooms, their books. Necks may go unwashed, bodies unbathed, but never do they neglect their beloved bicycles. They rub, scrub, and polish for hours, until the things sparkle like the Crown Jewels! Clearly, no boys had flung the bicycles inside—gangsters had! With a good food supply, what better hideaway than the deserted school? I rode back, alerted the town policemice, and we moved in. Outnumbered, the gang gave up. They'd ambushed the lads and forced them back to the school."

Hollyer beamed. "Brilliant, sir! Congratulations! Good luck on your secret mission to Mexico!"

"The hour grows late, Dawson. We'd best depart."

On our doorstep waited thirty-two thankful dentists who paid Basil a princely fee, promised us free dental care forever, and waved as we dashed down Baker Street in the swirling fog.

Our destination—a people's ship bound for Mexico!

Cluster 2

At the Bottom of the Sea

EUGENIE CLARK

Dr. Eugenie Clark is a Japanese-American marine biologist who has had many adventures while exploring the world's oceans in search of rare and unusual fish. In this excerpt from her book *Lady with a Spear* she describes her first diving experience.

La Jolla, California, is a few miles south of Scripps Institute of Oceanography. I was in a restaurant gobbling down a hamburger sandwich with a fat slice of raw onion. My stomach, tight with excitement, gave little digestive assistance. Today I was going to walk on the sea bottom in a diving helmet. Dr. Hubbs had practically promised it. I hurried out of the restaurant, got on my motor scooter, and putt-putted through La Jolla on my way back to the Institute.

It was always nicer going back, downhill most all the way. The weak motor of the scooter never conked out. I could ride along easily and take in the beautiful coastal scenery of southern California. You could see the Institute from town. Its white buildings sparkled in the sunlight, and today, at the end of the pier, the Institute's research ship, the *E. W. Scripps*, lay at anchor waiting for us.

A diver who had worked with the Navy was going to give instructions and a diving lesson to four Scripps students. Dr. Hubbs, an experienced helmet diver, was going to use the helmet to explore the kelp beds off La Jolla and I tagged along as his general assistant, hoping to have a chance to use the helmet too.

When we were anchored off the kelp bed, our instructor from the Navy gave us a briefing on the signals used underwater—standard Navy signals for helmet divers with no system for speaking to the ship.

One tug on the signal cord by the diver tells the tender, "I'm all right." Two tugs mean, "Give me more line, I'm going farther away." Three tugs tell the tender, "Take up slack in line, I'm coming in closer." And four tugs mean, "Danger, pull me up fast."

"Be sure you have these signals straight," the instructor cautioned. "And remember, the job of the tender is very important. Every diver should learn to tend lines to get the feel of the signals from both ends. The tender should give the line a single tug every now and then which asks the diver if he's all right and then the diver should answer to reassure the tender.

"The bottom here is about twenty-eight feet, which means you'll have nearly two atmospheres of pressure in your lungs from breathing the air we pump to you at that depth. If for any reason you have to 'slip' your helmet and come up without it, be sure to let that compressed air out of your lungs as you're rising. There's a valve on the right side to regulate the amount of air you're getting.

"O.K., who wants to go first?"

I looked at Dr. Hubbs anxiously but he motioned to me to wait.

The first student went down. He wore just bathing trunks and sneakers. He walked down the ladder on the side of the ship. When he was up to his neck in water, they lowered the heavy helmet onto his shoulders. He was down only a few minutes, but several of us took turns tending his line at least long enough to give it one tug and get his answer, which was hard to distinguish from the pull and bounce of the ship. He came up

wide-eyed. "The water's a bit cold and eerie down there but it was wonderful."

The second man wore slacks and a shirt. He said he wanted to stay down longer. But when he reached the bottom of the ladder, some feet underwater, he climbed up again. "I'm afraid my sinuses can't take it." He was really disappointed.

"Let Genie have a try," I heard Dr. Hubbs saying to the instructor. And in a few minutes I was on the ladder, lowering myself into the cold water while the weight of the helmet flattened the goose bumps on my shoulders.

Once the helmet was completely submerged, it rested more comfortably. When I reached the bottom rung of the ladder I could see under the ship's hull and I glanced around. I was over a thick bed of kelp. The ends of the long strands of orange-brown seaweed reached up through the murky green water just to my feet, as if I were standing on the tops of trees in this strange underwater forest. Every now and then, the kelp tops bent in unison like long grass in an open field when

a breeze passes. I could feel the shift in the water current too. It was like a cold draft. I wished I had worn more than just my bathing suit, for any clothing, though it be soaking wet, is considerable protection against the winds of the underwater world.

I grabbed the rope hanging beside the ladder and let myself slide down it into the heart of the kelp forest. I started walking along the sandy bottom of the sea among the waving kelp fronds that now stretched high above my head. The ship's keel looked far overhead. What a lot of fish down here and how close they came to inspect this slow-moving intruder they did not seem to fear.

One bold fish came right up to my helmet and looked in at my face.

"Shoo," I said, rather startled. A strong and unpleasant odor hit me in the face. The klunking sound of the air pump filled the helmet. The close air in the small space now had the smell of rubber from the life line mixed in unpleasant combination with something else. I finally identified it. "Well, Genie, I hope you remember not to eat onions with your hamburger before your next dive."

The kelp was thick around me. It was dark and cold and indeed eerie. I headed for a more open sandy area,

51

shimmering in filtered sunlight. I felt a tug on the signal cord and gave one back. But they tugged again and again, in spite of my answers, until finally I gave one big pull, almost falling over in the process—and then the line was still. It took more force than I thought to make them feel my answer.

Everything was fine now except for my breathing. The air was heavy and I was breathing with difficulty. I opened the air-regulating valve a little and, with relief, felt the air grow fresher. But still, breathing under two atmospheres of pressure and walking with this clumsy weight on my head was far from comfortable.

The sand suddenly moved under my foot and a flounder scurried out of my way. There was a dark mass ahead of me and I headed toward it. But my line was taut and held me back. I backed up a few steps to get a better grip, and then I gave two heavy yanks on my signal cord. I felt a loosening as the tender gave me more line.

Walking toward the dark mass, I got close enough to see that it was a cluster of rocks. It had holes in it like windows, and lovely lavender sea anemones, abalones, shellfish, and sponges decorated it. It was like coming across a gingerbread house in this water forest. But there was no telling what witch of the sea might live here, so I decided not to go too close. I walked around it.

The kelp thinned out and sharp rocks protruded from the sandy bottom. I walked on, poking at brown starfish, sea cucumbers, and a keyhole limpet with a black velvet mantle covering its whole shell except for the "keyhole." I tried to catch some of the close-swimming fish in my hand.

Suddenly I looked up and saw the kelps far away bending toward me in a low bow. The bow traveled quickly forward through the kelp bed and I braced myself, bending my helmet and leaning forward as one would to buck a strong wind. And it was well I did, for a strong underwater current swept by with great force. I was mentally patting myself on the back for being so well prepared when I was completely knocked off my feet, almost losing the helmet, by the returning current that had sneaked up from behind me. I learned to expect and respect the return and about-face of tidal currents. The sea was growing rougher but I went on, spellbound by the magic all around me.

Soon I was not just breathing heavily but actually gasping. I opened the air valve some more but it didn't help. I opened it more and more until it seemed to be completely open, but the gasping grew worse. My head started getting groggy and I realized something was very wrong.

I hadn't exchanged signals with my tender for some time. Better give those four tugs. I reached for the signal cord. It hung loosely down my side to the sea floor. I turned around in panic and saw to my horror the slack line, yards and yards of it, lying along the sea floor in the meandering path I'd come along. It looked like a long snake coiled around the rocks and the footholds of the kelp. I lifted it up and pulled but a coil caught on a rock. I started to retrace my steps back toward the ship as fast as the clumsy helmet would let me move. It was like trying to run in a nightmare, where your legs will only move in slow motion.

My breath grew shorter, my eyes burned, and my head felt numb. I seemed to struggle along miles of my lifeless life line before I finally saw the hull of the ship. It was still some distance away, but the line was taut here. My arms and legs were turning to rubber, but with a last surge of strength I gave one good tug. Then I felt myself fainting.

The feeling of fear had left me and a sweet sickness seemed to have replaced it. Slap-happily I thought of the irony of the situation—the meaning of my last desperate tug for help—"I'm all right."

I had fallen to my knees, kneeling over in the sand. In this tipped position, water began coming into my helmet. It was cool and refreshing and knocked some sense into my stupid head. I slipped the rest of the heavy helmet off and let the buoyancy of my body carry me upward. Up . . . up . . . through the green atmosphere like a balloon. My mouth had opened involuntarily to gasp in whatever medium was available, air or water, like a blowfish in a desperate situation. But I could take nothing in. The air in

53

my lungs came gushing out in one long continuous belch as the surrounding pressure decreased.

When I hit the surface, I saw a shower of swimmers dive over the side of the ship. Dr. Hubbs, wearing frog's feet, reached me first. I got a glimpse of his worried face and felt his strong hand grab my hair and tow me toward the ship.

They wrapped me in blankets and the cook brought me a cup of hot coffee. "What happened?" they wanted to know. I told them about the air seeming insufficient and opening the valve to let more in. "Just like a beginner to screw the valve the wrong way and cut off the air," someone remarked. But Dr. Hubbs and the instructor were checking the helmet and found the valve open fully. It turned out that the air line just above the helmet had been recently mended with a garden hose attachment, and this had come loose. I had been losing most of the air pumped to me before it had reached the helmet.

"It's an awful thing to have happen on your first dive," Dr. Hubbs said sympathetically. "There's only one way to help erase such an experience."

And so, when the helmet was
fixed, and after a short rest which
didn't allow my fears to become too
deeply rooted, I went down again.
This time, as with the dozens of
helmet dives I have done since, there
were no mishaps or onion-scented air.

55

See Along the Shore

MILLICENT E. SELSAM

The sea is beautiful to look at. Its blue waters sparkle in
the sunlight or turn to lead under a gray sky. It is red under
the setting sun and gleams like gold in the moonlight.

But the sea and the shore near it are more than just
beautiful. They are places of discovery.

At the seashore you can see that the world is round.
Watch a ship get smaller and smaller as it leaves shore
and goes out toward the horizon. If the earth were flat, you
would see all of the ship until it went out of sight.

But notice what happens. As the ship reaches the
horizon, you see only the smokestacks. The curve of the
earth hides the lower part of the ship. The ship moves on,
and you see only the smoke.

Stare into the flames of an open fire of beach driftwood.
The fire glows with strange colors. A flash of blue or green,
and a startling red now and then, makes this kind of fire
different from all others.

The colors come from ocean salts that soaked into the fibers of the wood when it floated in the sea. For the sea is a rich mineral soup. Most of it is plain sodium chloride—the salt we use for our food. But there are also salts of almost every chemical element. Copper salts and salts of boron give the flames a green color. Calcium salts glow orange-red. Once in a while you will see violet—the color potassium salts give.

The salts of the sea have come from the land. For millions of years the rains falling on the rocks of the earth have dissolved minerals and carried them down by rivers to the sea. Occasionally volcanoes have erupted and poured minerals from deep in the earth directly into the waters of the ocean.

Let the sand on the beach pour through your fingers and think about time. For it has taken millions of years for these tiny particles of sand to reach the beach you are sitting on.

57

High up on mountains the wind, sun, and rain combine to break off pieces of rock and tumble them down. The tiniest pieces of rock—sand grains—are washed downhill and find their way into streams.

Years may pass before the grains of sand reach a river. In the moving water of a river the grains travel on. But how slowly! It may take a million years for the sand grains to move a distance of a hundred miles. Finally they reach the sea. There the waves pick them up and carry them from one place to another along the beach.

The sand that runs through your fingers comes from far away and long ago. It tells you something of the great age of the earth we live on.

Did you ever have to pick up your towels and lunch basket and move higher up on the beach because the tide was coming in? The waters of the sea are always moving up the shore and then slowly back again.

Mark the high-tide point on the beach with a stick. Note the time this point is reached. Do the same the next day. Does high tide come at the same time as the day before? Continue your observations for a few days. You will notice that high tide comes about fifty minutes later each day.

Long ago, before the time of calendars and clocks, people who lived near the sea and gathered their food from it noticed this same thing. The high-tide point came later each day. They noticed, too, that the moon rose later each day. They began to think that there might be some connection between the moon and the rise and fall of the tides.

Much later this was proved to be true. We know now that it is the moon that pulls the waters of the earth toward it and makes them bulge into a high tide. The sun pulls on the waters of the earth too. But it is much farther away, and its pull is therefore not as strong as the moon pull.

If the moon stayed in the same place, the tides would come at the same time every day. But the moon moves. It circles around the earth and makes one complete turn every month. Each day we see it rise fifty minutes later than the day before, because it has moved that much farther in its path around the earth. And each day the high tide comes fifty minutes later than the day before.

It is easy to see why the part of the earth under the moon has a high tide, but why is there a high tide on the side of the earth opposite the moon? Scientists tell us that the moon pulls the earth away from the water on the opposite side and makes the waters there bulge into a high tide too.

At the seashore you can learn about the tides. You can sift through the treasures the sea throws on the beach. You can discover why driftwood from the sea glows with strange colors in the fire. You may wonder about sand and where it came from. You will see a world of constant change.

Escape to Freedom

KENNETH FRANKLIN

"Smalls, today and Saturday are going to be busy days," stated Captain Relyea, captain of the Confederate gunboat *Planter*. "We have to go down the Stono River and pick up some guns at Cole's Island. The guns are needed for Fort Ripley, in case the Union forces get past Fort Sumter."

"Yes sir, Captain," replied Smalls, the black pilot for the *Planter*. "You can count on us to get the job done." Smalls spoke calmly, his voice hiding the real excitement that ran through him.

Months before, a plan had formed in Smalls's mind—a plan that would carry his family and him to freedom. The American Civil War was a little over a year old. All along the Atlantic Coast, slaves were being freed by Union forces. Outside the range of Charleston's guns a Union blockade kept the Charleston harbor locked. If only he could get his family and crew safely to the Union forces. . . .

He would wear Captain Relyea's wide-brimmed straw
hat and stand in the pilot's cabin. Under cover of
darkness sentries could easily mistake him for the
swarthy Captain Relyea.

But he had to get ashore and tell Hannah. She would
have to be ready to go at a moment's notice. The families
of the crew would also have to be told when and where
they were to go to board the *Planter*.

"Captain, I know we are rushed, but I was wondering if I could go ashore and see Hannah and the baby before we sail?" asked Smalls. "He hasn't been well, and it'll be a few days before I see them again."

"Smalls, it's against regulations to let you go, but we can't leave for another two hours. So I guess it's all right. But be back in two hours," warned the captain.

Bob Smalls ran down the gangway and headed for his home. As he walked past the idle merchant ships, Smalls noted the position of each one. The *Etowan* is the best, he thought. The deck hands will hide the women and children until we take them on board the *Planter*.

Reaching home, he ran quickly up the stairs. "Hannah," he cried excitedly as he ran into the room. "Be ready to go on Monday night! While the Captain and his mates are at that fancy ball for the naval officers, we can sail to freedom aboard the *Planter*."

"But Bob, it's so dangerous," cautioned Hannah.

"No more so than staying in Charleston as slaves, wondering if we're going to be penned up somewhere. I was born a slave, but I aim to live or die a free man rather than as a slave in Charleston."

The excitement in his voice and the shine of freedom in his eyes carried away Hannah's fears, and she knew that despite the dangers, she would follow Bob.

Quickly Bob explained the plan and gave her directions on how to get to the *Etowan* and whom she should talk to. "Tell the others that once they start, there is no turning back," said Bob. "If caught, we are going to scuttle the ship and jump into the bay. I have to get back to the ship now. I won't have a chance to see you until Monday night when you come aboard ship. Be careful!"

Hours later Smalls noted the details of the harbor more closely than he had ever done before. For the last six years he had been a pilot guiding boats through the treacherous waters of the harbor. He knew every nook and cranny, every current of waters in the bay, but he wanted to be sure. This time everything his family and the crew had hoped for would rest on Smalls's ability to guide the *Planter* through the night past the sentries and the guns of the mighty forts.

"Smalls, get your men ready," ordered Captain Relyea. "We're coming into Cole's Island now. You and the men are to start dismantling the guns and carrying them to the pier."

The rest of Friday and all of Saturday was spent in bringing the guns down to the pier. Captain Relyea kept after the men to hurry, but nothing seemed to go right.

Sunday the *Planter* sailed back to Charleston without the guns. As the boat pulled into her berth, Captain Relyea called Smalls over. "Make sure we have a full supply of wood for the return trip to Cole's Island tonight. We have to get the guns loaded tomorrow and unloaded at Fort Ripley by evening. The mates and I want to attend the dance tomorrow evening."

The men under Smalls's direction soon had the ship ready to sail. Wood and supplies were aboard, and all the equipment needed to load the heavy guns was checked over. Sunday evening the *Planter* sailed again for Cole's Island.

Monday, May 13, 1862, dawned bright and clear. Captain Relyea felt confident that he would be able to get the guns loaded and transported to Fort Ripley and still get back to Charleston.

But plans other than Captain Relyea's were also in effect. All day the men worked to load the cannons. Nothing seemed to go right for them. Ropes would come loose and a cannon would slip back down to the pier. Alfred Gradine slipped and work stopped to check his twisted ankle. But he was soon on his feet, working with only a slight "limp."

"Smalls!" bellowed the Captain. "What are you men doing down there? This isn't a picnic. Get busy on that tackle!" Turning to his first mate, Captain Relyea grumbled, "A good whipping probably wouldn't hurt any of that crew. We'll never get those cannons to Fort Ripley tonight."

Late Monday afternoon Smalls called up to the Captain, "We're all set, sir."

"It's about time too," cried Relyea angrily. "Get this ship under way. We won't make Fort Ripley tonight; we'll just make it back into Charleston."

"Yes sir, Captain. I understand. The men just haven't been feeling right. But a good rest in Charleston will put them back into shape. They'll be different men by this time tomorrow," Smalls replied calmly.

As the steamer moved out into the Stono River, it seemed that the crew began to move faster and with more confidence than they had all day. Everything was running according to plan.

That evening the *Planter* was left in Smalls's command. The ship was silent except for the creak of boards and the gentle slap of water against the sides. The four-man crew—Robert Smalls, his brother John Smalls, Will Morrison, and Alfred Gradine—sat quietly awaiting the night. There were food supplies and plenty of wood for the boiler. Each man sat with his own hopes and fears.

Darkness settled over Charleston. "All's well!" came the sentry's cry. Darkness fell deeper across the harbor.

Shadows began to move aboard the *Planter*. Smalls and Gradine broke into the Captain's cabin and found guns, charts, and the broad-brimmed hat—the hat that would be their ticket through the blockade or to burial.

"All's well—eleven o'clock," cried the sentry.

A thin cloud of smoke floated out of the stack. The *Planter* backed carefully away from the wharf and out into the harbor. The darkened ship moved slowly past idle merchant ships. No challenging cry came from the sentries.

"John, we're over the first hurdle," Smalls said. "Now, help Will get the boat ready. He'll row over to the *Etowan* and pick up the women and children."

"O.K. But shouldn't we wrap the oars so they don't squeak as he rows?" asked John.

"Good thinking. We don't want to disturb any guards that might be on the other ships. Remember, we're all dead men if we get caught," warned Bob.

The *Planter* stopped and anchored close by the *Etowan*. Soon the boat was in the water and on its way to pick up the families of the crew. The *Planter* pulled against the anchor chain as if she, too, wanted to be away from the danger.

The men strained to see through the dark night. Where was the boat with their families? Had the plan been discovered? Should Bob sink the ship and all their hopes for freedom?

"I think I hear them," whispered Alfred. The muffled sounds of a boat cutting through the water reached the *Planter*. "But are the women and children in it?" he asked cautiously.

"*Planter*. Ahoy, the *Planter*," came Will's voice.

"It's them. Get 'em aboard ship quickly," ordered Bob. "Then get a full head of steam up." Smalls felt like cheering, but any celebration would have to wait until they were all safely away from Confederate control.

The anchor was raised. Smoke poured out of the stack as the *Planter* swung out into the main harbor current. Fort Ripley loomed off to the left. The fort's sentries watched. The *Planter* moved quickly past and they thought nothing about it.

Fort Johnson on the right was passed without a challenge. The pounding of the steam engine and the rush of water past the ship's hull were the only sounds heard aboard the *Planter*. Even the children sensed the danger and sat quietly in the quarters below deck.

Bob Smalls stood quietly at the window of the

pilothouse. "I'll have to take us through the shallow channel between Fort Sumter and Morris Island," he said to John. "There are too many obstructions in the channel between Sumter and Fort Moultrie."

The eastern sky was beginning to show signs of the morning as the *Planter* steamed slowly toward Fort Sumter. Would there be too much light when they approached Sumter? thought Bob. What if there are new orders about travel or possibly a new password? Despite these fears, Smalls kept the ship heading toward the huge guns of Sumter.

Bob turned the wheel over to John and leaned on the window sill of the pilothouse. He pulled the brim of the straw hat lower so that his face was shadowed in the dim light of dawn that seemed to get ever brighter. "Keep her steady as she goes," said Bob calmly. "We're almost in hailing distance."

Reducing speed as required by naval regulations, the *Planter* pulled to within voice range of the sentries. His stomach knotted, Bob reached for the cord to the whistle. Three short blasts and then one long hiss of escaping steam.

"The gunboat *Planter* has given the proper signal," cried the sentry.

"Pass the *Planter*," replied the corporal of the guard.

"We have passed," Smalls called down to the crew. In the engine room and below decks the crew and their families stifled cheers of celebration. Albert and Will shoved more wood into the furnace. The steam pressure began to climb. Smoke poured from the stack as the *Planter* gained speed.

One mile—Fort Sumter's guns were being left behind. Ahead lay the safety and freedom of the Union blockade.

The sentries stared at the speeding *Planter*. "Corporal of the guard! Corporal of the guard!" cried the sentry. "Something is wrong about the *Planter*!"

Bob and his crew heard the call to arms at Sumter, but the call came too late. Safely out of range of the huge guns the *Planter* and her crew were gone.

Bob steered for the Union forces, heading for the lead ship. Down came the Confederate flag and up went a white bedsheet—a flag of truce.

But the Union ships were turning their guns on the speeding *Planter*. Bob heard the sound of drums.

"What does it mean?" asked John.

"Those drums are calling the men to their battle stations," replied Bob. "I hope we aren't going to be blown out of the water this close to freedom." Turning to look up at the truce flag he exclaimed, "No wonder they have their guns on us! The flag isn't billowing out and they can't see it in this early morning light."

69

Then as though the free winds heard him, a breeze rippled the waters and lifted the sheet out for all the Union ships to see.

The Union commander ordered his men to hold their fire. "Ahoy steamer. Who are you and what is your business?"

"The *Planter* out of Charleston come to join the Union fleet!" cried Smalls over the cheers of his crew. The race for freedom was over. The crew and their families were free.

The story of Robert Smalls could have ended at that point. But on that spring night in 1862, Robert Smalls sailed into the pages of history. He served the Union forces throughout the remainder of the war. After the war he worked to build a better government for all the people of South Carolina. Even up until his death in 1915, Robert Smalls was a constant champion for freedom. Born a slave, he kept his promise that he would die a free man.

Horses

A young lad and an old man,
The ebb and flow of life,
Stepping out together.
'Horses, Gran'pa, will the
Horses be there today?'
'Ay lad! Today, yesterday and tomorrow,
The horses will be there.'
'Tell me again how they will look, Gran'pa.'
'How they will look, boy?
Well, today they will have caught
The spirit of the wind.
They will prance and leap and race.
Over the rocks they will gallop, heads
Held high with tossing manes.
White horses, lad! Fiery! Strong!
They will race to meet us, with foam
At their nostrils.
And we will hear them come,
Feel their pounding under our feet.
Then they will turn, lad, curl and whirl away.
They'll go back and return again.
Ay, lad! There will be white horses
On the sea today!'

—Lynne Williams, age 13

Shipwreck

VERA CUMBERLEGE

Jim waked. He clutched the bedclothes up to his chin and lay listening. His bed trembled as the gale battered the house. But the noise of the storm had not waked him, nor was it the distant roar of the waves pounding the shore. It came again, the sound that had waked him, deep and insistent, the boom of the lifeboat gun, calling the lifeboat crew to its work.

He jumped out of bed, groped for the door, and flung it open. A light showed under the door opposite, and he crossed the landing and burst in. The candle by his parents' bed was caught by the draft and went out. A match scraped, and his father's shadow sprang up the wall, his head looking like a bird with a large beak—but the beak was only the sou'wester that his father had pulled on and was now tying under his chin.

"You are dressed already!" Jim could never understand how his father got into his oilskins so fast, for he never seemed to hurry. "I won't be a moment, Father. Wait for me," he begged.

"No, Jim." His mother was sitting up in bed. She spoke firmly. "No, it's dark. We would only get in the way."

The shadow on the wall nodded, and Jim felt a hand ruffling his hair. Then his father was gone. Even the sound of his boots on the stairs was lost in the rattle of the windows and the banging of his bedroom door.

It was hard for Jim to go back to his room, knowing that he must miss seeing the lifeboat launched. He loved watching his father and the other men high above him with their oars ready. Down below, men would push the boat from its shed, starting it down the slipway to meet the waves. In a smother of foam the oars would rise and fall, and the dangerous moment would pass.

A new lifeboat was due any day. A powered boat with an engine to do the work of oars. It would be launched from its own pier beyond the breaking waves.

Jim had told his father that he hoped the new boat would not come, for it would make the launching dull. He thought it could never be as exciting as men with oars pushing out against the sea. His father had made no reply.

Jim dressed quickly, and he and his mother met in the kitchen where the steady flame of the oil lamp made the room seem calm after the wild shadows thrown by his candle.

"There is no need to gobble your breakfast, Jim. It will be too dark for an hour yet."

Jim glanced up at his mother. He was not taken in by her quiet way of talking. He knew she was afraid. He wondered if she would be afraid when he joined the lifeboat crew. She had no need to be, for they had both seen the lifeboat launched in stormy weather and return safely many times.

"I wonder what boat is in distress and where it is," he said.

"The wind is from the east," his mother said. She looked at the barometer. "I've never seen the glass so low. Lord have mercy on those at sea!"

Jim thought of the jagged remains stuck fast below Culver Cliff, and the rusty iron in White Cliff Bay among the seaweed-covered rocks. They had been there all his life and were the remains of ships that had run for shelter and been caught by a wind and tide too strong for them. This might be yet another. He must get down to the lifeboat station. Since he had not seen the launching, he must see the return. He peered through the window. Behind the racing storm clouds, there was a greyness in the sky.

"Let's go," he said.

His mother was packing a basket—tea, sugar, milk; cups folded in a cloth. Then she buttoned up her coat and blew out the lamp.

Old men in oilskins, wet with spray, were on the slipway watching the great waves come rolling in. Too old to pull an oar, they waited, hoping for a chance to lend a hand when the lifeboat returned.

Jim tugged at a wet sleeve. "Mr. Bevis!" he called.

The old boatman looked down at him, then walked to the lee of the lifeboat house, where they were out of the wind. "You won't see nothing from here," the old man said. "She is stuck fast beyond the foreland. They are taking the rocket up there now. Drat my rheumatics."

"I'll go and see what is happening," Jim said. Then he felt his mother's hand on his arm. "I'll be all right. I won't go near the edge," he assured her.

"There is quite a crowd up there already," old Bevis told her. So she let him go.

As he left the shelter of the boathouse, the wind caught and held him. He had to bend double, butting through the wind, as he started up the long slope to the foreland from where he would see into White Cliff Bay.

Before he was halfway, he had to drop onto his knees and turn his face from the wind, to get his breath. Then he glanced seaward to see if the wreck was in sight, and his mouth opened and the wind drove back his cry. He clutched the turf, choking and breathless, for he had caught a glimpse of the lifeboat among the waves. As he watched, he saw it rear up from a deep trough, climbing so steeply he was sure it must turn over. But it perched for an instant on the top before plunging down the far side. The waves surged past and over the boat. The men strained at the oars, yet Jim could see that they were making no progress. All of their combined strength was not enough to drive the boat around the foreland in the teeth of such a gale. In sudden panic he thought that if they tired, they too might be swept onto the rocks.

He would have stayed where he was on the soaking grass if some boys from the village had not come by and swept him along with them. As they went through a little wood of stunted trees, they shouted to him not to worry. Beyond the trees they met the full force of the gale. A group of people was standing bunched together, all leaning forward as if the wind was a solid wall.

Jim screwed up his eyes against the salt spray that whirled over the cliff edge, stinging his face. Through the spray he could see a small ship wedged on the hidden rocks. Though lashed by the storm it still held together, still looked like a ship with a smokestack and wheelhouse, only its angle was wrong. It was tilted sideways, with the remains of a boat dangling from its side.

Suddenly a wave sprang up beyond the stern, towered over the ship, broke, and smothered her. A dark form was swept over the bow and hurled toward the shore. It was a man. The crowd made a queer gasping noise, then everyone was running in an odd, slow way, pushing at the wind, forcing a way through. They went down the steps by the coastguard cottages and stumbled through the stones, hurrying along the beach. A wave crashed on the shore and foamed toward them. The group clung to the slippery lumps of chalk at the base of the cliff as icy water drenched them and filled their shoes. Then the water ran back, dragging stones and seaweed with it. Jim grasped a hand and found himself part of a human chain. The leaders were wading into the sea, trying to reach the dark form. It was first carried toward them and then swept back from their outstretched hands. At last a limp body was brought ashore and carried up the beach. Jim struggled back through the shifting stones to the wooden steps.

Out on the reef the ship listed still further and now Jim could see a group of men in the bow holding on grimly as the waves pounded over them. Up by the wheelhouse another sailor appeared, turning his head as though searching for a way to reach his companions. Then another great wave rolled over the ship and thundered toward the shore. The crowd came pushing by him up the steps, bearing the drowned man in a rug, and when Jim looked again toward the ship, he saw that half the wheelhouse had been torn away. From a broken railing there seemed to be a spider hanging from its thread, but he knew it was the sailor he had seen a moment before. As another wave curled over the ship Jim shouted, "Hold on!" though no one could have heard his shout. The wave must have lifted the man upward, for now he was stretched flat against the rails with nothing below him but the cruel sea. Jim suddenly understood

that it was for this that his mother had been afraid, for an unknown seaman in peril. Soaked to the skin and shaking with cold, Jim clung to the steps, waiting to see the lifeboat reach the ship. But it never came. What will happen to the sailors? he thought. Where is the lifeboat?

A gun cracked above his head and a line flew through the air and fell across the bow of the wreck. It was the rocket old Bevis had spoken of. Now the sailors could be hauled to safety. Would it save the man on the rail? A shaft of sunlight cut through the black clouds and for a moment the broken rails gleamed white. Then they were hidden under a curtain of falling water, but not before Jim had seen that the sailor was no longer there.

He stumbled up the steps. At the top he looked back once more, but nowhere among the breakers could he see a dark form; no swimmer appeared among the wreckage. Jim put his hands over his ears to shut out the sound of the waves and the mocking wind, and turning his back to them, he ran.

The lifeboat was back on the slipway and the men were inside the boathouse when Jim got back. The words he was going to shout at them slipped from his mind, for in a shocked moment he thought they were all dead. Utterly exhausted they sat unmoving; only his father raised an eyebrow. Jim answered his unspoken question.

"They got a line across the bow with the rocket," he said. "They got it there at the first try."

A man slumped in a chair got to his feet, and life seemed to flow back into all of them as they turned toward him. "First try did you say?" When Jim nodded, the man went on, "Who said George was no good? Him and his wind pressures. Drift and thrust. Yes, thank ye, I'll have a cup of tea."

Talk and argument and the rattle of teacups. Jim stepped back into a dark corner. With cold hands he felt for the muscles in his arms. Through his sodden coat he could feel how thin he was, how small his muscles were. Even if he grew to be as strong as his father, he could still be too late—too late to reach a drowning seaman.

Suddenly he remembered the new lifeboat that was due any day. The powered boat whose engines would drive her through the fiercest gale. The boat he had thought would make a rescue dull. With the new boat we should get there in time to save them all, he thought. Perhaps I won't have to wait till I am as strong as Father.

The Coral Reef

GILDA BERGER

Look out over a coral reef and you will see coral shaped like rocks, stars, fingers, or fans. There is coral shaped like animal horns and antlers, and even like trees and bushes. There is coral of all colors—tan, orange, yellow, purple, green, and pink.

A coral reef is an underwater range of stone hills. It forms in the shallow, warm oceans of the world. A warm water-temperature and a good supply of sunlight are needed for the coral to grow. Over thousands of years it is built up, bit by bit, by the remains of sea plants and animals. The largest coral reef in the world is the Great Barrier Reef off the coast of Australia. It is hundreds of feet wide and more than a thousand miles long.

Coral reefs take a constant pounding from the waves that hit against them. But these moving waters make the reef a wonderful place for plants and animals to live.

The waters bring a rich supply of food and oxygen to the reef. And they carry away carbon dioxide and other waste products.

Dive down and you will see thousands of different sea plants growing in, on, and around the reef. There are many more that you cannot see. These are tiny, invisible specks floating in the water.

Many animals live around the reef. There are sponges, anemones, and clams that are fixed to one place on the coral. They depend on the rushing waters to bring them food. There are starfish, sea urchins, lobsters, and crabs that creep and crawl over the reef looking for food among the coral. And there are fish who swim in and out of the tunnels, caves, and passages in the coral.

If you get to know the plants and animals on a coral reef, you will find that each has its place on the reef, each is fit for its way of life on the reef, each depends on the reef, and

80

each depends on others that live on the reef.

All coral reefs are made up of layer upon layer of the stony skeletons of animals and plants that once lived there. Covering these skeletons is a thick layer of small, living animals known as coral polyps. The coral polyps are the most important animals on the reef. They are the reef-builders.

A reef begins to form when one floating polyp attaches itself to a piece of rock in the water. The polyp is a small, colorless blob of jelly, no bigger than your fingernail. As soon as it is in place, the polyp starts to grow a skeleton around itself.

81

This skeleton takes the shape of a little cup around the lower part of the polyp. It protects the polyp in the same way that a suit of armor protects a knight. It is made of a kind of stone called limestone. The limestone skeleton is made from chemicals that the animal takes in from the water.

During the day the polyp stays safely inside its skeleton. But at night it stretches out its tiny arms, or tentacles, and catches and eats the smallest animals that drift by in the water.

After a while the coral polyp sends out a branch, or bud. The bud attaches itself to the rock next to the parent polyp. It starts to grow. It builds its own cuplike skeleton.

More and more polyp buds form. They build their stone houses alongside the others. Soon the mass of coral skeletons grows quite large. New polyps start to grow on top of the older polyps. The older ones die as they are covered over by the new ones. But their skeletons remain. These layers of polyp skeletons make up most of the coral reef.

But a reef made up only of coral skeletons would not be very strong.

It would crumble under the battering of the ocean waves. Other animals and plants that come to live on the reef help make it stronger.

The sea cucumber helps to make the reef more solid. This cucumber-shaped animal lives in the mud and sand around the reef. It takes in large grains of sand and broken pieces of coral while looking

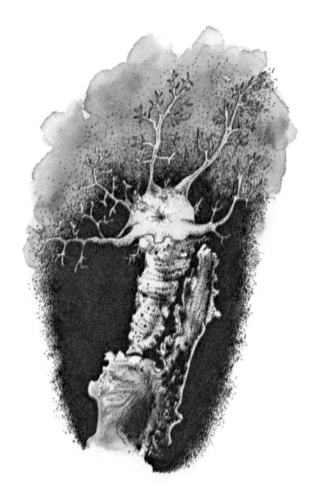

for bits of food. What it cannot eat, it spits out as fine sand. This sand fills in the empty cracks in the reef.

Tiny microscopic plants known as algae do the most to cement the reef together. There are many kinds of algae. Each kind is a different color and gives the coral one of its varied hues.

One type of red algae forms a layer of limestone that covers the coral skeletons and glues everything together into a solid mass. It covers the skeletons of sponges, starfish, and sea urchins that are added to the reef when they die. It attaches the shells of clams and oysters to the reef.

Algae have neither roots, stems, nor leaves. They are too small to be seen without a microscope. Like other plants they take in carbon dioxide and give off oxygen. They depend on the living coral, which like other animals takes in oxygen and gives off carbon dioxide.

If you could look inside a coral polyp, you would see many thousands of microscopic brown algae living there. The polyp provides a home for the algae. It protects them. A coral polyp that is short of food will sooner evict the algae than eat them.

The algae remove the coral polyp's wastes by taking them in as food. They also take in the waste carbon dioxide produced by the polyp. And they give off oxygen, which the polyp needs in order to live and grow. Without the algae the polyps would grow much more slowly.

The way that the coral polyp and algae help one another is an example of mutualism. In mutualism, two different kinds of living things help each other. Both get along better as a result.

The anemone—a brightly colored animal that looks like a flower—and the crab also depend on each other. Sometimes a few small anemones attach themselves to an empty snail shell that is a home to a hermit crab. Often a hermit crab carries an anemone in each claw. The anemones frighten off the crab's enemies with their poisonous tentacles or help the hermit crab to capture its food. The anemone is then able to live on leftovers from the crab's food supply.

Sponges are other animals that

shrimp. The new shrimp are small enough to leave. They move out and some settle inside other sponges somewhere else on the reef.

The many species of fish that live on the reef match the varied colors of the coral, from bright green to brown, tan, red, pink, and purple. Their markings and bright hues confuse their enemies. It is hard to discover their odd shapes among the many twists and forms of the coral. These camouflages protect them from the larger fish that prey on them.

Reef fish are also equipped with spines, poisons, and other means of defense. Porcupine fish can inflate themselves so that they are hard to

stay fixed in one place on the reef or grow on snail-shell houses. They live on algae that they filter out of the rushing waters. A sponge provides shelter for many reef creatures. A scientist once counted more than seventeen thousand worms, crabs, fish, and other animals living inside one large sponge!

One of the most interesting tenants of a sponge is the snapper shrimp. The young shrimp comes into the sponge on the tide. It eats food found inside the sponge. It grows bigger and bigger. Soon it is too big to leave the body of the sponge. In time it gives birth to new

snatch. The stonefish sits on the ocean floor looking like a rock in the mud. Anything that lands on it is poisoned by one of the thirteen spines on the fish's back. And the mottled-gray skin of the sand flounder helps it blend in with the sand in its hiding place between the coral growths.

Typical reef fish are about nine inches long. Although they are of many shapes, they have narrow bodies, broad tails, and stubby fins. They are well fitted for life on the reef. They can swim fast, change direction quickly, and get around the rough coral easily.

Life on a reef is full of danger. Most of the fish on a reef eat other fish who live there. The biggest fish, the sharks and the barracuda, eat the snappers. The snappers eat the smaller mackerel, the mackerel eat the still smaller herring, and the herring eat the very small fry.

And many kinds of fish eat the coral polyps. The parrotfish scrapes and bites the coral all day looking for the juicy polyps. The bumpfish looks for polyps in the pieces of coral that it knocks off the reef with the noselike bump on its head.

Worms, snails, and starfish make holes in the reef as they search for the polyps.

Raging storms and pounding waves also break off pieces of coral. Sewage and other pollution are more recent dangers to the reefs. Where the polyps die, the reefs are often torn apart.

A coral reef is one of the most varied, crowded, busy, exciting, and challenging environments on earth. It is an ever-changing wonderland of colors and shapes and forms. It is rough and rugged, and at the same time it is delicate and fragile. But most of all, a coral reef is a closely woven community of millions of well-adapted plants and animals that depend on each other and on the reef for their survival.

Even as reefs are destroyed in some places, they continue to grow in others. There are reefs that are more than fifty million years old. They grow where there is enough food, light, and oxygen for all the creatures that live on the reef. And they keep growing as long as the tides and the temperature of the water do not change.

The Sharks

Well, then, the last day the sharks appeared.
Dark fins appear, innocent
as if in fair warning. The sea becomes
sinister, are they everywhere?
I tell you, they break six feet of water.
Isn't it the same sea, and won't we
play in it any more?
I liked it clear and not
too calm, enough waves
to fly in on. For the first time
I dared to swim out of my depth.
It was sundown when they came, the time
when a sheen of copper stills the sea,
not dark enough for moonlight, clear enough
to see them easily. Dark
the sharp lift of the fins.

—Denise Levertov

86

Sunday for Sona

GLADYS YESSAYAN CRETAN

Sunday had always been Sona's favorite day. Every Sunday the Baronian family—Sona's uncles and her great uncles, her aunts and her cousins—gathered at Sona's house because Nana lived there, and Nana was now the oldest member of the family. Besides, Sona's house had the largest dining room, and this meant that everyone could sit together for Sunday dinner, with only a little squeezing.

Sona had never wanted to miss any part of family Sunday. But now she had something else she really wanted to do, something she thought about all the time—sailing.

Since the first time she had gone to the nearby harbor with her friend Tommy to look at his uncle's sailboat, she had hardly been able to think of anything but the slap of the water against the boats and the tangy smell of salt in the wind.

Now Sona and Tommy worked on the *North Star* every afternoon. They helped with the sanding, the painting, and the varnishing. Uncle Jerry O'Brien finished rerigging the tall mast. The boat was seaworthy again. They could chug out of the harbor into the bay and then hoist their sails as they had watched so many others do. Sona and Tommy would become real sailors.

87

If only Nana would understand. "If you want to go and see the boat, fine," Nana said. "But why must you sand and paint?"

"Because," Sona said, "whoever helps repair the boat gets to go for the first sail. Mr. O'Brien bought it from another man, and it needs lots and lots of paint and varnish. Then we're going to sail it right into the bay, Nana."

Nana was stunned. "Into the bay?" she said and shook her head. "Your mother and father are trusting me to raise you safely. The bay sounds dangerous. I must think. We will say nothing to the family until I have decided if it is yes or if it is no."

Several weeks went by. Nana still hadn't decided whether or not Sona could go. Sona knew she couldn't wait much longer, because Mr. O'Brien had said she absolutely had to have her family's permission. Or better yet, one of them could come along. Otherwise she couldn't go on the maiden voyage of the fresh new *North Star*. What if she couldn't get Nana's permission?

Sona tried to ask on Monday. The words wouldn't come out. She tried on Tuesday. Nothing happened.

On Thursday she closed her eyes and thought the words for the hundredth time. She must have said her thoughts out loud, because she heard Nana answering, "No! No, I have decided against it. To sail into that great bay! In a tiny boat! Do you think we found you on the streets, to take such a chance with you?"

"It's not a chance," Sona said. "Mr. O'Brien has sailed clear around the world, and he's been training us."

89

Nana kept rolling out some dough. She said nothing.

"Besides," Sona went on, "Mr. O'Brien knows we both can swim, and by Sunday he'll buy some new life jackets."

Nana's rolling pin stopped. "Sunday?" she exclaimed. "Did you say Sunday?"

"Mr. O'Brien said it would be after church," Sona said in a tiny voice.

"Certainly. After church," Nana said. "But what of dinner? What of the family?"

"We'll try not to be back too late," Sona said miserably. "You said you would really think about it."

"Yes," Nana said, "and I am a lady who keeps her word. I have been thinking about it. About sailing, which is hard enough, and about meeting Mr. O'Brien. But not about changing our whole family life. No. That is too much."

No. That was the answer.

After all the scraping and sanding and painting. No.

After all the dreams of sailing with the wind. No. And after those dreams of faraway, mysterious ports. Just plain no.

On Sunday as Sona set the large dining room table, she could hear her mother and her grandmother bustling about in the kitchen. When she heard the noisy sizzling and gurgling of food cooking and the clatter of baking tins pulled from the oven, she ran quietly down the stairs. She ran past the apartments, past the houses, till finally, out of breath, she came to the docks. She really had run away to sea!

She stood at the pier to catch her breath and watched the boats, large boats and small, rising and falling in the water. They looked so comfortable, so exactly right. Then why did she feel so exactly wrong?

Because I know I shouldn't be here, she thought. But she knew she couldn't stay away either.

Down the docks she saw Mr. O'Brien and Tommy, arms full of the great bulky sails, starting to attach them to the mast.

Mr. O'Brien would feel sure she had permission to sail. He would never guess. . . . She decided not to think about it. She couldn't. It was too mixed up.

She ran toward the boat. "Here I am!" she called.

"Ah, the crew," said Jerry O'Brien. "Welcome aboard! Can you handle the jib?"

"Sure!" said Sona. She shook the jib sail out of its bag and clambered over the top of the cabin. She snapped the jib onto the tall forestay.

"Good work," Mr. O'Brien said. "You remembered everything. I hope someone from your family is coming."

"Well," Sona said, "well . . ."

"Sona!" Tommy called. "Is that your grandmother walking down the dock?"

"It can't be!" Sona said. She pulled her breath in. It was.

There was Nana, in her black coat and her little black hat, scarf blowing in the wind. There walked Nana, her back straight and her step brisk.

"Say," Mr. O'Brien said. "It's good of her to come to see us off. I'll feel better, too, knowing her personally."

Sona didn't answer. She slid down into the cockpit and peered out. She wondered if there was a better place to hide. She couldn't face Nana.

"What's she carrying?" Tommy asked.

"That's her satchel," Sona said.

"What's in it?" Tommy asked.

"Sometimes treats," Sona said. "But I don't think she'll have treats today."

"Why not?" Jerry O'Brien said. "It's a special day."

Nana looked carefully at each boat she passed. She came nearer and nearer. It was getting too late for Sona to run. But suddenly she did run. Straight to her grandmother.

"Oh, Nana," she said as she threw her arms around her. "I'm sorry. I shouldn't have run away!"

Nana looked down at Sona's face and nodded gently. She put her satchel down and gave Sona a hug. For a long moment neither one spoke.

"Never mind," Nana said finally. "I have been wrong too. I know you have never deceived me before. So I had to think what has driven you to it this time. I know, I left you with too hard a choice. And we did not talk about it enough. Now, never mind. I have come to see this *North Star* and to meet the sailor, O'Brien."

"A pleasure, ma'am," called Jerry O'Brien. "I hope you'll sail with us."

"There is room?" Nana asked.

"Certainly," Jerry O'Brien said. "Sails four easily. Even five."

"Oh, Nana," Sona said. "You don't have to. Not for me. I don't think you'll like it."

Nana looked at her sternly. "I came to this country on a big ship," she said. "I sailed before you were born."

"Good for you," said Jerry O'Brien. "That settles it." He reached out and helped her onto the boat. "Welcome aboard," he said.

Nana opened her satchel and pulled out a brightly wrapped bottle. "I thought we might have a christening ceremony," she said.

"You mean break the bottle?" said Sona. "On our fresh paint?"

"Maybe splinter the wood?" Tommy said.

"Perhaps we could drink a toast instead," said Mr. O'Brien.

"Exactly as I thought," said Nana. She handed each one a small paper cup. "We have grape juice," she said. "Sona's favorite drink."

"Ma'am," said Jerry O'Brien. "My hat's off to you. You've thought of everything. Tommy, get your harmonica. We can't have a celebration without music."

He lifted his cup. "Happy voyages, *North Star*," he said. They stood in place as Tommy played "Anchors Aweigh."

Nana smiled. "Good," she said. "A song of the sea."

Now Tommy started the motor and Mr. O'Brien took charge of the tiller, steering the boat past the row of small boats at the dock.

Nana and Sona sat opposite each other. "Beautiful," Nana nodded, as they looked ahead at the opening sight of the bay.

"Wind's perfect," Mr. O'Brien said. "Man the tiller, Tommy, and I'll hoist the sails. Hold her into the wind."

93

In a moment the white sails rose. First the large mainsail, then the smaller sail, the jib. With the motor turned off now, the boat began to rock with the waves and the wind.

"Look at that," Nana said. "Like wings."

"See, Nana," Sona said. "Over there is the Golden Gate. You go through there and on to the South Seas. Maybe to Tahiti."

"Wind's shifting," Mr. O'Brien said. "I'll take the tiller again. Sona, you're in charge of the jib. Now as I call, let the jib go. Ready about! Hard-a-lee!"

The small sail swung around to the other side of the boat.

"Tighten the jib sheet!" called Mr. O'Brien. "Pull!"

The ropes bit into Sona's hands. She pulled as hard as she could and finally made them fast to a cleat on the deck.

Nana moved quickly from her seat to the one across. "Balance the weight," she said.

"Mrs. Baronian," said Jerry O'Brien, "you are a natural sailor."

"Certainly," said Nana.

"Coming to a choppy patch of water," said Jerry O'Brien.

"Good," Nana said.

The boat rolled and tipped. It found its balance again.

"Good," she said again. "Now we are matching wits with the sea."

Sona couldn't believe it. She had gotten her wish; she was sailing. And Nana was there, too, enjoying every minute of it.

Cluster 3

A Successful Halloween

E. L. KONIGSBURG

On Halloween night our family rushed through supper. But the trick or treaters started coming even before we finished. Most of the early ones were bitsy kids who had to bring their mothers or fathers to reach the door bells for them.

I didn't tell my parents about Jennifer. I mentioned to my mother that I was meeting a friend at 6:30, and that we were going to trick-or-treat together. Mom just asked, "Someone from school?" And I just said, "Yes."

The days start getting short and the evenings start getting cool in late October. So I had to wear my old ski jacket over my Pilgrim costume. I looked like a Pilgrim who had made a bad trade with the Indians. Jennifer was waiting. She was leaning against a tree. She had put on stockings. They were long, black, cotton stockings, and she wore a huge, black shawl. She smelled a little bit like moth balls, but I happen to especially like that smell in autumn.

"Hi," I said.

"I'll take the bigger bag," she replied.

She didn't say "please."

I held out the bags. She took the bigger one. She didn't say "thank you." Her manners were unusual. I guessed that witches never said "please" and never said "thank you." All my life my parents had taught me a politeness vocabulary. I didn't mind. I thought that "please" and "thank you" made conversation prettier, just as bows and lace make dresses prettier. I was full of admiration for how easily Jennifer managed without bows or lace or "please" or "thank you."

She opened her bag, stuck her head way down inside, and said:

Bag, sack, parcel post,
Fill thyself
With goodies most.

She lifted her head out of the bag and tightened her shawl. "We can go now," she said.

"Don't you mean 'Bag, sack, parcel, *poke*?' " I asked. "Parcel *post* is the mail; *poke* is a name for a bag."

Jennifer was walking with her head up, eyes up. She shrugged her shoulders and said, "Poetic license. *Poke* doesn't rhyme."

97

I shrugged my shoulders and started walking with her. Jennifer disappeared behind a tree. No master spirit had taken her away. She reappeared in a minute, pulling a wagon. It was the usual kind of child's wagon, but to make the sides taller, she had stretched a piece of chicken wire all along the inner rim. Jennifer pulled the wagon, carried her bag, clutched her shawl, and clop-clopped toward the first house. I walked.

I had been trick-or-treating for a number of years. I began as a bitsy kid, and my mother rang the door bells for me, as other parents were ringing them for those other bitsy kids that night. I had been a nurse, a mouse (I had worn my sleepers with the feet in), and other things. I had been a Pilgrim before, too. All I mean to say is that I'd been trick-or-treating for years and years and years, and I'd seen lots of trick or treaters come to our house, but I'd never, never, never seen a performance like Jennifer's.

This is the way Jennifer operated: 1. She left the wagon outside the door of the house and out of sight of her victim. 2. She rang the bell.

3. Instead of smiling and saying "Trick or treat," she said nothing when the people came to the door. 4. She half fell against the door post and said, "I would like just a drink of water." 5. She breathed hard. 6. The woman or man who answered would say, "Of course," and would bring her a drink of water. 7. As she reached out to get the water, she dropped her big, empty bag. 8. The woman or man noticed how empty it was and said, "Don't you want just a little something?" 9. The woman or man poured stuff into Jennifer's bag. 10. The woman or man put a little something in my bag too. 11. Jennifer and I left the house. 12. Jennifer dumped the treats into the wagon. 13. Jennifer clop-clopped to the next house with the bag empty again. 14. I walked.

Jennifer did this at every house. She always drank a glass of water. She always managed to drop her empty bag. I asked her how she could drink so much water. She must have had about twenty-four glasses. She didn't answer. She shrugged her shoulders and walked with her head up, eyes up. I sort of

98

remembered something about a water test for witches. But I also sort of remembered that it was something about witches being able to float on water that was outside their bodies, not water that was inside their bodies.

I asked Jennifer why she didn't wear a mask. She answered that one disguise was enough. She told me that all year long she was a witch disguised as a perfectly normal girl. On Halloween she became undisguised. She may be a witch, I thought, and, of course, she was a girl. But perfect, never! And normal, never!

I can say that Jennifer collected more treats on that Halloween than I had in all my years put together including the time I was a mouse in my sleepers with the feet in. Because I was with Jennifer each time she went into her act, I managed to collect more treats on that Halloween than I ever had before, but not nearly as many as Jennifer. My bag was heavy, though.

Jennifer and I parted about a block from my apartment house. My bag was so heavy that I could hardly hold it with one hand as I pushed the button for the elevator. I put the bag on the floor while I waited. When the elevator arrived, I leaned over to pick up my bundle and heard my Pilgrim dress go *r-r-r-r-r-i-p*. I arrived at our apartment, tired and torn, but happy. Happy because I had had a successful Halloween. Happy because I had not met my enemy Cynthia on the elevator. And happy because my costume had ripped. I wouldn't have to be an itchy Pilgrim another Halloween.

Secret Codes and Private Post Offices

KATHLEEN LEVERICH

There are times when secrets are important, times when you must tell someone something without others understanding what you are saying. Maybe you're planning a surprise party for your grandmother's birthday, discussing what to get your brother for Christmas, or simply talking to your best friend about private matters.

Soldiers, spies, and diplomats have had this problem for centuries. Especially in times of war, they need to tell their friends and allies secrets that their enemies must not hear. They have found a solution. They don't talk at all; they send messages written in code.

You can make up your own code for important private messages. Here are some suggestions for simple ways to begin.

1. Choose a color code. For example:
   red = most important
   yellow = good news
   black = danger

You can write the whole message in the color that fits. Or you can just make a mark of that color on the message after you've folded it up. Then your friend will know what kind of news to expect just by looking at the note.

101

2. Choose key words and sentences. Then pick other words to replace them in your messages. For example:

For	Use
I must see you	giraffe
mother	rose
father	anchor
teacher	bell
call me on the phone	the sun is out
don't tell anyone	crocodiles like gumdrops
one or one o'clock	January
two or two o'clock	February
[and so on]	

Using this code, you could write messages such as the following: Giraffe at May. The bell is talking to my rose today. The sun is out to say okay. Remember, crocodiles like gumdrops!

Your friend would know you meant: I must see you at five o'clock. The teacher is talking to my mother today. Call me on the phone to say okay. Remember, don't tell anyone.

3. If you need to use words that are not part of your code, you can spell them backwards or scramble the letters.

4. Choose a place to use as a private post office. Then there will be less chance of your message falling into the wrong hands. Some possible private post offices are a tree hollow, a crack in a stone wall, or a book that no one ever takes from its shelf.

5. As a final precaution, you can write in invisible ink. You will need the following things:

lemon juice   a toothpick
a cup   a sheet of plain white paper

Put the lemon juice into the cup. Using the toothpick as a pen, dip into the lemon juice and write your message on the paper. Be sure to keep the toothpick damp; dip it often into the lemon juice. When the juice dries, the writing disappears. To make the message visible, hold it close to something hot—a light bulb or a radiator or an iron. Don't use a match, a candle, or any other flame; your message could go up in smoke. As you slowly heat the paper, you will see brownish writing begin to appear.

Milk is also a good invisible ink. To make milk writing visible again, you must rub it with graphite powder. Pencil lead is made of graphite. To get graphite powder, scrape the lead with a knife or scissors.

Two Fables

MIRRA GINSBURG

How the Peasant Helped His Horse

A peasant drove to market to sell his grain. The roads were bad, and his horse got tired pulling the heavy load. The peasant saw that the horse could not go much farther. He took one of the bags of grain from the cart, put it across his shoulders, climbed back into the driver's seat, and said to the horse, "Giddy-up, giddy-up! It's easier for you now! I am carrying a whole bag on my own shoulders!"

Three Rolls and One Doughnut

A peasant walked a long way from his village to the city. By the time he got there, he was very hungry. He bought a roll and ate it, but he was still hungry. He bought another roll and ate it, but he was still hungry. He bought a third roll and ate it. He was still hungry. Then he bought a doughnut. He ate it—and what do you think?—he was not hungry any more.

"Ah!" He clapped himself on the forehead. "What a fool I was to have wasted all that good money on rolls! I should have bought a doughnut to begin with!"

A Man Who Made Use of His Shadow

JULIA E. DIGGINS

This is the story of Thales, a man who found a use for his shadow. Thales was born about 600 B.C. in the Greek seaport of Miletus on the Aegean Sea. Miletus was a crossroads for trade caravans from the East Indies and ships that called on the bustling ports of the Mediterranean Sea.

Although the caravans and ships brought exotic goods to Miletus, Thales was more interested in the traders and sailors who told stories of strange lands and strange people. He heard tales of the amazing cities on the banks of the Tigris, Euphrates, and Nile rivers. He listened in awe to accounts of the great scholars who could measure the movements of the moon and the stars in the sky.

Young Thales yearned to travel. His mind was filled with questions about the world and the universe— questions to ask the learned men he had heard about. But travel cost money, and Thales had none.

"Anybody can make money if he puts his mind to it," Thales decided.

Then he saw the silvery leaves of the olive trees on the hillside and thought about the oil in the fruit of those trees. Olive oil was used in lamps, for cooking, and as a soap and skin softener. But the orchards hadn't produced olives for several seasons. No one knew what was wrong or could tell when the olives would grow again. Thales decided to find the answer to the problem.

He studied the weather conditions of the past years and discovered a pattern. The pattern pointed to good weather for the next season, which meant that the orchards should start producing olives again. Thales decided to take a chance. He quietly visited each olive grower and asked to buy his press. The growers were delighted to sell their presses because they had been useless for several seasons.

The following season, however, the big crop came, just as Thales had predicted. Thales owned all the presses. So he pressed the olive oil and earned enough money to travel and study.

He journeyed first to Babylon, which was already an ancient city in 600 B.C. In the library of Babylon, Thales found the drawings of the stargazers. He spent weeks studying and copying the drawings and finally discovered patterns that enabled him to predict eclipses.

Because of this knowledge, Thales was able to predict the eclipse that occurred while the Medes and Lydians were in the sixth year of a stubborn war. The armies were so frightened by the strange darkness that they stopped fighting. Afterwards, Thales was called "One of the Seven Wise Men of Greece." By discovering the pattern of eclipses, Thales had helped thinking

107

people to look for other orders and patterns in the universe.

Leaving Babylon, Thales sailed into the broad Nile River which flowed through a patchwork design of vast fields laced by irrigation canals. At last he reached Egypt and began his studies there. He went from Memphis to Thebes, from temple to temple, and stopped wherever wise men gathered. The priests and scholars guarded their knowledge jealously, but Thales was clever. He encouraged them to show off their knowledge. Eventually they showed him their "magic shadow stick." The stick was held upright on the ground so that it cast a shadow exactly equal to its height. The height of much taller objects could then be found by simply pacing off the lengths of the objects' shadows.

Thales did not believe in magic. He was convinced that there must be a reason behind this "magic." He experimented and studied until he found the pattern.

When he visited the ancient pyramids in Egypt, Thales wanted to measure the height of the largest and most famous, the Great Pyramid, the pyramid of Cheops. Thales and his teachers arrived at the Great Pyramid late one afternoon. A group

of Egyptian priests were paying their respects to Cheops, who had died and been buried in the pyramid thousands of years before. These priests had a low opinion of the Greeks, who did not have a tradition of learning as old as theirs, and hoped to trick the foreigner with their questions.

"Do you know the magic of the shadow stick?" they asked.

"Yes," Thales answered.

"Then tell us the height of the Great Pyramid." Thales showed no sign of confusion even though he did not have the shadow stick. He knew his own height. He could see that his shadow on the ground was twice as long as his height. Therefore, he thought, the pyramid's shadow must be twice as long as the pyramid's height.

Thales measured the length of the pyramid's shadow. The shadow was 992 feet long. He divided 992 by 2 and answered, "The height of the Great Pyramid is 496 feet."

The priests were dumbfounded and embarrassed. Thales' teachers were dumbfounded and delighted. Thales' logical reasoning had answered questions that all the learning of ancient Egypt had not. His discoveries marked the beginning of Greek geometry.

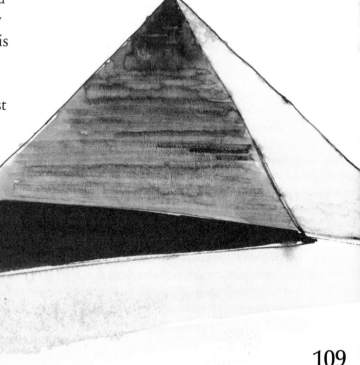

109

Thales continued to ask questions. "How is the world supported in space? What makes the weather change?" He thought long and hard about these and other questions. Some of Thales' answers to questions such as these were right; some were wrong.

But the truth or falseness of Thales' ideas was not as important as his search for the truth about the world and the universe. Thales asked questions and offered ideas. He encouraged others to do the same; he even encouraged his students to disagree with him. This was the first time that people discussed basic ideas about the world in this way. Under Thales' leadership a new tradition of learning developed in Greece and spread throughout the entire Western World. He is often remembered as the Father of Philosophy.

110

The Snail's Monologue

Shall I dwell in my shell?
Shall I not dwell in my shell?
Dwell in shell?
Rather not dwell?
Shall I not dwell,
shall I dwell,
dwell in shell,
shall I shell,
shallIshellIshallIshellIshallI . . .?

(The snail gets so entangled with his thoughts or, rather,
the thoughts run away with him so that he must postpone
the decision.)

—Christian Morgenstern
German poem translated by Max Knight

111

Mouse Woman and the Tooth

CHRISTIE HARRIS

There was a rumor about Mouse Woman.

It wasn't one of the stories they told about her in the feasthouses. It was just a rumor that the old people whispered to one another when they were chuckling together about things *they* had done in their own childhood and when they were remembering the stories *they* had made up to get themselves out of trouble. And they didn't actually believe the rumor.

After all, who could think that Mouse Woman had ever been anything but the spirited, imperious little busybody they all called Grandmother? Who could ever think she had once been a girl-narnauk playing with other children? And who could ever ever think *she* had once made up a story to get herself out of trouble? Or had even gotten into trouble in the first place?

"Of course, it's only a rumor," they reminded one another. And anyway, it had happened—if indeed it had happened—in the time of very, very, very Long Before. Long before some of the Real People had migrated southward along the coast to build their handsome totem-pole villages. Long before Mouse Woman herself had moved southward into the Place-of-Supernatural-Beings to watch the world with her big, busy, mouse eyes.

According to the rumor, the small-girl-narnauk named Mouse Woman was living with her Mouse People relatives far to the north. And one day she was out playing with the other children. According to the rumor, she was running and squeaking and catching a streaming kelp bulb when one of her playmates noticed something.

"Mouse Woman!" the friend squeaked. "You've lost a tooth."

"Yes," Mouse Woman agreed. And she clamped her mouth shut to end the conversation.

"But it wasn't even loose yesterday," her friend insisted. "It wasn't wiggly or anything."

"Wasn't it?" Mouse Woman asked, as if she couldn't quite remember.

"So! What happened to your tooth?" the friend insisted.

"Well . . ." Mouse Woman looked up at the sky while she tried to think of a good way a small girl could lose a tooth that hadn't even been loose or wiggly the day before. And looking at the sky, she suddenly thought of Envious-One, the mischievous little being who was always doing something spiteful to children. Or at least he was always being blamed for doing something that a more proper little being would never have done.

"Envious-One did it," Mouse Woman announced.

"Oh!" her friend squeaked. "What did he do?"

"Well . . ." Mouse Woman went on, quickly thinking what Envious-One could have done. "He shot at me from the sky and knocked out my tooth with one of those little arrows."

"Oh!" The friend looked properly indignant about Envious-One's dreadful deed.

114

"And it hurts terribly," Mouse Woman went on. For she was beginning to enjoy her own story. "In fact," she went on, "I think I'm going to die." She put both hands over her mouth to prove that it hurt so terribly that she might even die the way the Real People died.

"Oh!" her friend squeaked, looking even more indignant about Envious-One's dreadful deed. "Well you mustn't die outside." So putting an arm around her hurt friend, she led Mouse Woman into the house.

"My dear! What has happened?" Mouse Woman's mother cried out.

"Envious-One did it," the friend said. "He shot at her from the sky and knocked out her tooth with one of those little arrows."

Mouse Woman showed her teeth to prove that he had indeed done the dreadful deed.

"Lie down, my dear!" her mother said. And she covered Mouse Woman with a rabbit-skin robe. "We'll send for Grandmother."

"Oh, no!" Mouse Woman squeaked. "I mean . . . please don't trouble Grandmother!" Grandmother was a wise old woman with very, very sharp eyes.

But her mother sent for Grandmother.

"My dear! What has happened?" Grandmother asked when she saw Mouse Woman lying under the rabbit-skin robe.

"Envious-One did it," Mouse Woman's mother answered. "He shot at her from the sky and knocked out her tooth with one of those little arrows."

Reluctantly Mouse Woman showed her teeth to prove that he had indeed done the dreadful deed. But she quickly shut her mouth and her eyes too, with the pain of it all. For Grandmother had very, very sharp eyes.

"We must do something about this," Grandmother announced. "Fetch me a drum, Ermine Woman!"

Ermine Woman fetched her the drum, and Grandmother began to beat on it very, very softly, for spirit guidance.

Then she stopped drumming. "First, we must find the tooth," she announced. And she sent Ermine Woman to tell all the small children in the village to search for the lost tooth.

They searched and searched and searched and searched. But no one could find the lost tooth. And they all went back to the house with Ermine Woman to report to Grandmother.

"Fetch me the drum again, Ermine Woman!" Grandmother ordered.

Ermine Woman fetched her the drum, and once again Grandmother began to beat on it very, very softly, for spirit guidance.

Then she stopped drumming. "Perhaps I can find the tooth," she said, "for I have very, very sharp eyes. Come with me, Ermine Woman, while the children wait here with Mouse Woman."

And off they went. The children waited in the house with Mouse Woman, who seemed to be looking more and more distressed, as if indeed she *might* die the way the Real People died.

"Ermine Woman," Grandmother said. "I think our small girl has been pilfering the stone pine-nut cakes." For it was well known that Mouse Woman was very, very fond of stone pine-nut cakes. Grandmother led the way to a small house where many food boxes were stored.

"Search in that box!" Grandmother ordered, pointing to a large box of stone pine-nut cakes.

So Ermine Woman searched. And by and by she held up a small, hard cake that had been well nibbled around the edges.

Grandmother took the nibbled cake. "Now find the tooth!" she ordered.

And Ermine Woman found the tooth. It was right near the spot where the hard little cake had been nibbled.

"I think our small girl has been pilfering the stone pine-nut cakes," Grandmother said. And though her eyes twinkled a little, her voice was very stern. For greed was the Great Sin—especially for a young person as high-ranking as Mouse Woman.

They went back to the house with Grandmother hiding the nibbled cake under her fur robe, and Ermine Woman holding up the lost tooth.

"You've found her tooth!" several children squeaked. And they crowded about to see it.

117

Mouse Woman shut her eyes *not* to see it. And now she was looking even more distressed, as if she might indeed die the way the Real People died.

"You've found her tooth!"

"We've found *a* tooth," Grandmother agreed. "But it may not be Mouse Woman's." After all, there were many small children in the room with teeth missing. So she ordered Ermine Woman to try it first in the tooth-gaps of the other children.

And Ermine Woman went from child to child, from tooth-gap to tooth-gap, trying to fit the tooth into the empty socket. But the gap was always too large or too small.

"Then it must be Mouse Woman's," Grandmother said. "Open your mouth, my dear!"

Reluctantly Mouse Woman opened her mouth. But she shut her eyes with the pain of it all. For Grandmother had very, very sharp eyes.

Ermine Woman placed the tooth in the tooth-gap. And it fitted perfectly into the empty socket.

"It's Mouse Woman's!" the children squeaked. "Where did you find it, Grandmother?"

"Where I found it, my dears," Grandmother answered. "Have no more concern for Mouse Woman. She will soon be well again. Go back to your game, children!"

So the children went out of the house to start running and squeaking and catching a streaming kelp bulb again.

"And now, my dear," Grandmother said, looking down at the small-girl-narnauk lying under the rabbit-skin robe. She showed the well-nibbled stone pine-nut cake.

"Yes, Grandmother," Mouse Woman squeaked in a very, very small voice. She looked up at the wise old lady with big, unhappy eyes.

"Guess where I found the tooth, my dear!" Grandmother ordered.

"With . . . the . . . cake?" Mouse Woman guessed, as if it might indeed be just a guess.

"With the cake, my dear," Grandmother agreed. And she went off.

"Well!" her mother said sternly when Grandmother had gone. "You have been pilfering the stone pine-nut cakes. You!" Her You! was a most indignant squeak. For it was well known that greed was the Great Sin. It was equally well known that a high-ranking girl must be an example to other people. And what girl among the Mouse People was as high-ranking as the girl who wore the great title of Mouse Woman?

"I might as well die," Mouse Woman squeaked, for it would be a dreadful thing if the other children ever found out that Mouse Woman was greedy. "What am I going to do?"

"Perhaps you should strangle yourself on a forked willow twig, my dear," her mother suggested, though of course she didn't mean it. It was just something Mouse People sometimes said to their children since it was well known that distressed real mice occasionally strangled themselves on a forked willow twig. It was equally well known that supernatural Mouse People could never die.

"That's what I'll do," Mouse Woman announced, suddenly leaping up. Thankful for a way to escape, she rushed out of the house. And she stayed away for a very, very long time. So they'd all be sorry. But at last she crept back into the house.

"I couldn't find a forked willow twig," she told her mother.

"Then perhaps we had better just forget all about it, my dear," her mother suggested.

And according to the rumor, Mouse Woman was very glad to forget all about it.

"Perhaps we had better just forget all about it, too," the old people whispered to one another.

But they never did. They just kept on whispering the rumor to one another when they were chuckling together about things *they* had done in their own childhood; when they were remembering the stories *they* had made up to get themselves out of trouble. Still, they never did actually believe the rumor.

Phoebe and the General

JUDITH BERRY GRIFFIN

The year is 1776. Thirteen-year-old Phoebe Fraunces has been sent by her father to be the housekeeper at Mortier House, George Washington's New York headquarters. Samuel Fraunces, owner of the Queen's Head Tavern, has learned of a plot against the general's life. Phoebe is to act as a spy and report to her father all she sees and hears. The only clue Mr. Fraunces has is that the plan is supposed to be carried out by a member of General Washington's bodyguard—someone whose name begins with T.

If Phoebe is successful, she and her father will save General Washington's life, and help America win its war for freedom. Phoebe knew that although she and her family were free, other blacks, who were slaves, would not share in the victory.

Up to now, Phoebe has found out nothing. All of General Washington's bodyguards seem genuinely fond of him. Two members of the bodyguard, however, do stand out from the others. One, Mr. Hickey, because he is especially nice. The other, Mr. Green, because he keeps to himself and doesn't say much to anyone. Phoebe has made up her mind to watch Mr. Green carefully.

Weeks went by. The beautiful house, once so strange to her, was now like a good friend. Phoebe enjoyed using the fine china plates and crystal glasses. She enjoyed serving the cook's deliciously prepared meals to General Washington and his important guests, while Pompey, the cook's son, followed solemnly behind with the saltcellar and peppermill.

She knew she was there to save General Washington's life. But as the days went by and she still heard nothing, she began to wonder if perhaps her father was mistaken. No one seemed to be plotting anything, and it was now the beginning of June. Phoebe had been at Mortier House almost two months.

121

Then one day, when she went to their meeting place, her father wasn't there. Phoebe stood a long time, waiting and wondering. Should she go to the Queen's Head or back to Mortier House? As she was trying to decide, she saw her father hurrying toward her. He looked very worried. For the first time he seemed not to care that people might notice them. He held her by the shoulders and looked into her face.

"Phoebe," he said urgently, "I have heard that General Washington will be leaving Mortier House in a very few days. The person known as T will act before that time. You must find out who it is!"

Phoebe's mind was whirling as she hurried back toward the house. She was frightened, but she was also determined. She *would* save General Washington! She had long ago figured that he would likely be shot. During dinner he always sat in a chair by the window. He would make an easy target for anyone waiting outside.

If only she could get him to change his place, away from that window! His good friend General Gates would be a dinner guest at the house this evening. Everyone else was part of the family or a member of the bodyguard. Over and over she said their names. No one's name began with T.

As she reached the kitchen door, she saw Hickey sitting on the steps. "Why are you so solemn, pretty Phoebe?" he asked.

"Oh, Mr. Hickey, sir," said Phoebe breathlessly. "I'm so worried . . ." She paused. She did need help! Should she tell him? Maybe he knew something or had seen something that had escaped her notice. After all, he was a member of the bodyguard—it was his job to protect General Washington. Her father's words came back to her. "Trust no one," he had said. "No one." She sighed. She'd have to keep trying alone.

"Well," said Hickey after a moment. "I've got something to bring a smile back to that pretty face. Fresh June peas for the general's dinner—first of the season! His favorite and mine—and enough for us both! Some friends of the king will be mighty hungry tonight!" He handed her a large sack, filled to the brim with pea pods. Phoebe smiled in spite of herself.

"Grown men—soldiers of the American army—stealing peas!" she said.

Hickey pretended to be hurt. "All right," he said, snatching the sack from her and holding it over his head. "I'll just throw them out to your chickens—"

"No, no, Mr. Hickey." Phoebe laughed. "Here—I'll fix them myself."

Hickey handed her the sack. "I'll be here to fill my plate at dinnertime," he promised.

All afternoon, as she went about her chores, Phoebe worried. How could she get the general's chair away from that window? She would have to stand in front of it, blocking the view from outside. But then, would someone shoot her? By the time dinnertime arrived she was almost sick with fear. She was in the kitchen with Pompey getting ready to serve the plates when a voice behind her made her jump. It was Hickey.

"I've come for my peas," he said softly.

"Oh! Mr. Hickey, sir!" she said. "You gave me such a start! I was—" She stopped and looked at him, even more startled. He looked ill? frightened? She couldn't tell which.

"Which is my plate, and which is General Washington's?" he said. "It wouldn't do for him to have more than me." He spoke quickly, without smiling this time.

"I never heard of such carryings on over a pile of peas!" Phoebe said. "This is the general's plate, and this is yours!" She turned away to fill Pompey's saltcellar and turned back just in time to see Hickey's hand move quickly away from General Washington's plate and slide into his pocket. Something winked for a second in the light—something shiny, like glass.

"What are you doing to General Washington's plate?" she said. "I told you yours is here!" She picked up the plate. Was it her imagination, or was there something grainy, like sugar, on the peas? Phoebe looked more closely, but as she looked, whatever it was seemed to have disappeared. An instant later she wasn't sure—had she seen anything at all? She thought of the window again and forgot about the peas. She had to serve General Washington.

Leaving Hickey standing in the kitchen, Phoebe nervously entered the dining room, Pompey following with the salt. As she walked toward the general, Phoebe looked at every face around the table. Some of the guests were talking, some merely smiling. None seemed nervous or frightened.

And then she noticed the empty chair. Who was missing? But even as she asked herself the question, she knew. It was Mr. Green. Was he outside the house, with a gun, waiting? General Washington was sitting by the window, as she had feared. He sat back easily in his chair, listening to something General Gates was saying. The window was open! As she went past, Phoebe looked outside anxiously. There was not a sound, not a shadow, not a movement. The green grass was smooth and unruffled. Even the leaves in the trees were still.

"Well, Phoebe!" General Washington exclaimed as she stopped beside his chair. "June peas! How did you get them so early in the season?"

"It wasn't me, sir," replied Phoebe, looking past him out the window. "It was your Mr. Hickey brought them in, fresh today. He says they're your favorite."

"And mine as well!" said General Gates. "Where is Mr. Thomas Hickey? I want to thank him!"

Phoebe started to put the plate down in front of General Washington. Then, in a flash, it came to her who she was looking for. Mr. Green was not hiding outside the window to shoot at the general. The person who was trying to kill him was here—in the kitchen! Phoebe stood like a stone, the

plate still in her hands. She saw Hickey again—Thomas Hickey—laughing and teasing, bringing her candy and ribbons and seed for her chickens. And then bringing June peas for the general and sprinkling them with poison! T was for Thomas, member of General Washington's bodyguard!

Still holding the plate, she whirled around. Pompey was waiting behind her. "Run!" she screamed. "Run! Get my father!"

Everyone stopped talking. Pompey looked at her in amazement. "Y-your father?" he stammered.

"Sam Fraunces! At the Queen's Head! Go!" And she stamped her foot. Pompey had never heard Phoebe sound like that before. He dropped the saltcellar and ran through the kitchen door.

127

Everyone in the dining room sat frozen. All eyes were on Phoebe. "General Washington!" she cried. "Mr. Hickey has put poison in your dinner! I saw him!" There was a gasp from the table.

"What jest is this?" roared General Gates, getting up from his place and reaching for the plate. But before he could take it from her, Phoebe ran to the open window and threw the whole plate out into the yard.

Now the dining room was in an uproar. Chairs overturned; wine spilled as the men jumped to their feet in confusion. Some ran toward the window where Phoebe was standing, as if they feared she might try to escape. Others started for the kitchen. Some ran to surround General Washington. No one knew what to do.

It was General Gates who first noticed the chickens in the yard. "Look!" he shouted, pointing out the window.

Three of Phoebe's chickens had come to peck at the peas she had thrown outside. Two had already fallen dead. The third was still moving its wings, but as they watched, it, too, grew still. The poison, meant for General Washington, had killed the chickens instead.

"Get Hickey!" bellowed General Gates, and members of the bodyguard rushed to obey. Minutes later Thomas Hickey was dragged in from the yard, his face white with terror. He had not been able to escape. Minutes after that, Sam Fraunces burst into the room. Phoebe was still standing by the window, shaking. He ran to her and held her tightly. Phoebe clung to him, burying her face in his shoulder.

"Well done, daughter," Samuel Fraunces said quietly. "Well done."

After the excitement had died down and Hickey had been taken away, General Washington came to speak to Phoebe and her father. "It's nice to know people whom I can trust," he said simply. "Thank you."

Thomas Hickey was tried and convicted of trying to kill George Washington. Seven days later he was hanged. As was usual in those days, everyone turned out to watch. No one knows whether Phoebe was there. No one knows what happened to Phoebe after that. But we do know that she was a good spy.

This Is My Rock

This is my rock,
And here I run
To steal the secret of the sun;

This is my rock,
And here come I
Before the night has swept the sky;

This is my rock,
This is the place
I meet the evening face to face.

—David McCord

130

The Mountain of Tears

Retold by PAUL DAVID MANDEL

Long, long ago, in ancient Japan, there was a mountain called the Mountain of Tears. At its top there was a canyon where the old men and women of the neighboring villages were taken when they reached the age of sixty. There they were abandoned and left to die. Of course, this was a very cruel custom and it caused much sadness among the people, but it was an old law, and no one ever dared to break it.

In one of the villages there was a young farmer named Yoshi, who lived with his mother named Fumiko in a poor, small hut. They both worked very hard, trying to scrape a living from their tiny plot of land.

One chilly morning as the two of them were out chopping wood for the stove, Fumiko said, "Tomorrow is the first day of spring."

"Yes, Mother," replied Yoshi. "There is much work to do in the coming weeks. But we are both strong and healthy, and this year, with a little luck, we shall have a good harvest."

"No, Yoshi," said his mother. "On the first day of spring, sixty years ago, my mother brought me into this world. And tomorrow, as is the custom, you must carry me to the top of the Mountain of Tears and leave me there to die."

At this Yoshi's heart grew heavy, and he spent the rest of the day in gloomy silence, trying to understand the reason of the old ways.

The next evening, when Yoshi and Fumiko sat down to their last dinner together, the old woman would not eat.

"Tonight, my son, you shall eat my share as well. I no longer need the food, and you must have extra strength to carry me to the top of the mountain." She urged her son to eat, but the food was like dust in his mouth and he could not take another bite.

When the sun had set, the two prepared to make their journey. The old woman took off her shawl and wrapped it around her son's shoulders. "Tonight, my son, you shall wear my shawl. The night wind is damp and cold and you must keep warm on the journey back home." At the door she took off her wooden clogs and set them on the ground. "Tonight, my son, I have no use for shoes. Take them and save them for the day when your own are worn out." At this Yoshi's heart began to break.

Then Fumiko climbed upon her son's back, and so the sad journey began. Up the trail they climbed, higher and higher into the heart of the mountain. The moon rose over the pine trees, and the unhappy pair cast a shadow like a strange, two-headed beast.

Halfway up the mountain the trail disappeared, and Yoshi had to make his own path. As he walked through the trees and shrubs, his mother broke off the tips of the branches.

"Mother, what are you doing?" Yoshi asked. "Are you marking a trail so that you can find your way home again?"

"No, Yoshi," she replied. "I am marking this trail for you."

When he heard these words, Yoshi's heart broke in two, and he said, "Mother, I cannot leave you on the Mountain of Tears. Although the law forbids it, I am going to take you home. You are old, but you are strong and kind. And even if you were feeble and weak, I would not leave you here to die."

133

And so they returned home that night, together. To make sure that no one knew what he had done, Yoshi hid his mother under the porch of their hut.

Spring arrived, and Yoshi spent each day in the paddies and fields, working twice as hard because he worked alone. And each night he crept under the porch with food and tea for his mother. There, in the dark, they would spend a few precious moments together.

Then one day the lord of the province, the *daimyo*, called all of the village farmers to his castle. The daimyo was a powerful man, who sometimes delighted in commanding his subjects to do very difficult tasks. On this day he told them, "You must each bring me a rope woven of ashes. If you cannot do this, you must forfeit a bushel of rice."

The poor farmers went home slowly; they knew they could never weave such a rope. When Yoshi crawled under the porch that night, he told his mother all that had happened.

Fumiko sipped her tea, thought a moment, and then said, "It can be done. First you must weave a rope of twine, as tightly as you can. Place it on a flat stone and burn it very carefully until it turns to ashes. Then you can carry the stone with the rope of ashes to the castle."

Yoshi did exactly as he was told, and the next day when the farmers gathered again at the castle, he was the only one who had a rope woven of ashes.

The daimyo was very pleased with Yoshi, but he commanded his subjects to do another task, to see if the young man was indeed as bright as he seemed. "You must bring me a conch shell with a thread passed through each of its spirals. Those who cannot complete the task must forfeit another bushel of rice."

Again the farmers trudged home, already defeated. How could anyone thread such a shell? And again Yoshi told his mother all that had happened.

Fumiko thought a moment, then she said, "It can be done. First you must put a piece of rice on the end of a thread. Then give the rice to an ant and make it crawl into the wide end of the conch shell. Point the narrow tip toward the light; the ant will crawl toward it, passing through each spiral on the way out. When the ant reaches the end, your shell will be threaded."

Yoshi did as he was told, and the next day, when the farmers gathered together, Yoshi was the only one who had been able to thread the shell.

The daimyo was very impressed and called Yoshi to his side. "Tell me, young farmer, how is it that you were able to perform such difficult tasks?"

135

In the presence of such a powerful lord, Yoshi's heart began to pound. He feared for his mother, but he was an honest man. He answered truthfully.

"Forgive me, your highness, for I have deceived you and disobeyed the laws of our land. On the first day of spring I was supposed to take my mother to the top of the Mountain of Tears and abandon her there, as custom requires. But she is such a good, kind person and I felt so sorry for her that I brought her back home and hid her under our hut. When you commanded us to do such difficult things, I asked my mother for advice. It was she who told me how to make the rope and thread the shell."

The daimyo was greatly moved by Yoshi's story. He remembered the sadness that he, too, had felt when he had carried his own father and mother up the Mountain of Tears.

"Farmer Yoshi," he said. "It is true that you have disobeyed the laws and traditions of our land. It was your duty to abandon your mother; you have failed in that duty. But your mother's wisdom teaches us a valuable lesson." The daimyo raised his voice so that all the farmers could hear. "One day each of you will grow old. Some will become weak and unfit for work in the fields, an extra mouth to feed and a source of worry to your children. But some will also have grown wise in those years, and the wisdom of old age is a precious thing that cannot be measured by bushels of rice. Therefore, I proclaim an end to the law of abandonment at the Mountain of Tears."

That night when Yoshi returned home, he led Fumiko out from under the darkened porch and into the lamplight of their hut. Then, together, mother and son celebrated their joyous reunion.

I Meant to Do My Work Today

I meant to do my work today,
But a brown bird sang in the apple-tree,
And a butterfly flitted across the field,
And all the leaves were calling me.

And the wind went sighing over the land,
Tossing the grasses to and fro,
And a rainbow held out its shining hand—
So what could I do but laugh and go?

—Richard Le Gallienne

Grandma's Secret

JOHN DANIEL STAHL

Jakey came running out of the pump house into the yard where Grandma sat husking corn. He held his hand out as if it were on fire and screeched like a stuck pig.

"Yelling won't help," Grandma said calmly. "What happened, Jakey?"

"A bee—" Jakey gasped. "I caught it, but it bit me." Then he began to scream again. Betty stuffed her fingers in her ears to shut out his yells.

Grandma laid aside her towel full of corn and took Jakey's hand. She examined the small red spot on his palm. "Here's the stinger," she said, pulling it out and showing it to Jakey. "That bee will die. A bee can't live without its stinger." She tweaked his nose. "But you'll live. Run inside and put ice on it. Soon it won't hurt, and then you can help us finish up here." She lifted the corn onto her lap again.

"How much do we have to do yet?" Joyce asked.

"Just three baskets and cleaning up—that's all," Grandma said, pointing at the scattered corn husks and the piles of fresh, beady corn. She wiped her forehead with the back of her hand.

I'm going to dream about corncobs tonight, Joyce thought. I'll be tearing open corn in my sleep. She gripped the fuzzy silk and forced the husk open, hearing the rubbery squeak of leaves against moist corn.

She looked at Grandma's hands. How old they look, she thought. Grandma's hands were wrinkled and crossed with veins, but they were strong, and gripped the corn firmly. Joyce stared at her own hands thoughtfully. What's it like to have old hands, she wondered.

A shimmer of haze rose above the fields at the horizon. The sun had beaten down from a cloudless sky all day.

"It's awfully hot," Betty said. "I can't wait to swim."

With the cool pond in mind, it didn't take long to husk the remaining ears and clean up the yard. The children changed into their bathing suits and tramped downstairs into the kitchen.

"Will you come along, Grandma?" Joyce asked.

"You can bring a rope and be our lifeguard," Betty said, laughing. "A lifeguard who can't swim."

Grandma only smiled in reply.

Joyce and Betty skipped through the field toward the pond, and Jakey ran to keep up. But Grandma walked leisurely and noticed that the sun had advanced far enough to lose its midday heat. She heard the distant drone of an airplane, then splashes and laughter from the pond. Joyce and Betty swam a race across the pond and back, while Jakey stood, bent over, looking between his legs at the reflection of

the farm on the hill—right side up because it was twice upside down.

"The water's wonderful," Joyce called to Grandma. "You should at least get your ankles wet."

"Come swim," Jakey said, making motions as if he were swimming in air.

"Try it, Grandma," Betty shouted. "Maybe you can learn to swim. Watch!" she yelled, and disappeared under the water. Just when Jakey began to wonder whether she had drowned, she came up with a big splash ten feet from where she had been. She snorted and pushed her streaming hair back out of her eyes. "We dare you to come in, Grandma," she said.

Grandma stood on the bank, looking at them. She did not answer. She smiled a little. Then she turned back toward the house. The children stood in the water, wondering.

"Where are you going, Grandma?" Betty shouted. Grandma merely turned and waved briefly, then went on, a frail figure in the sun-parched field.

"Do you think we hurt her feelings?" Joyce asked Betty, letting herself fall backwards into the water.

"I don't think so," Betty replied. "She's not that way."

"Then why did she leave?"

"Maybe to make supper. Hey, Jakey, that water's no good to drink!"

"Jakey!"

Jakey left off drinking pond water and began practicing his strokes. Betty and Joyce swam lazily, enjoying the cool water.

Suddenly Joyce stopped swimming and stood up. "Hey, look," she said, staring up the hill as if she were seeing an apparition.

Betty shaded her eyes to see better. It was Grandma, wearing what looked like pajamas. Betty and Joyce doubled up with laughter. Grandma paid no attention. Very calmly she walked down to the edge of the water, tested the temperature with her big toe, and stepped in. Before the children had time to catch their breath, Grandma was swimming a slow but skillful crawl across the pond.

Seeing the gray head moving across the rippling surface of the pond filled Joyce with a strange exultation. It was as if she were watching something as amazing as cows flying. She swam over to Grandma and laughed. "That swimsuit must be an antique! Where did you get it? Where did you learn to swim?" she asked. She felt as if she were about to burst. Grandma could swim!

Grandma looked at her with amusement. "I learned to swim as a girl, in my father's farm pond," she said.

"And you never told us!" Betty said, joining her sister.

Grandma only smiled and swam around them.

"Hurrah for Gram!" Jakey shouted.

Later they rested on the bank of the pond, feeling clean and comfortably tired. They smelled the rich pond and field smells and listened to the crickets.

Joyce looked at Grandma. There must be so much more about her that I don't know, she thought. Despite the floppy green-and-white striped swimsuit, Grandma looked dignified and serene.

"What's it like to be old, Grandma?" she asked.

Betty sat up on her towel and frowned at Joyce. "You shouldn't ask questions like that," she said angrily. "It's not nice."

Grandma looked at Joyce thoughtfully, as if she were reading something in Joyce's face, but she did not answer.

After supper was over and the dishes were washed, Grandma and the children sat on the porch with glasses of iced lemonade. At the horizon the sun lit a thin strip of clouds with flame colors. They listened to the squeak of Grandma's rocker on the porch floor and watched the first fireflies spark their signal lights across the lawn.

Joyce's tired muscles ached pleasantly, and she remembered with satisfaction the work she had done that day. There were the eggs she had gathered in the morning, the floors she had swept, and the long rows of corn she had "picked down." Evening is the best time of all, she thought.

"Evening is a remember time," she said aloud.

"That's what being old is too, Joyce," Grandma said quietly. "A remember time."

Joyce looked out across the lawn, past the huge shadowy trees that sheltered the porch, and imagined what Grandma was seeing. She might see people—invisible to Joyce— moving across the grass, talking and laughing; horse-drawn carts rattling up the lane in summer sunshine; a sudden thunderstorm fifty years ago, perhaps, or a calm evening just like this one.

"The past becomes a part of you," Grandma said.

"Do you think of Grandpa a lot?" Joyce asked. She saw Betty's disapproving frown, but decided to pretend she hadn't.

Grandma was silent. Her husband had been dead for two years now. "Grandpa is a part of me," she said after a little while. "I think of him as if he just went upstairs or around the corner. I'm remembering all the time," the old woman continued. "It's better than dreaming."

Joyce understood. She walked over to her grandmother and hugged her. "I want to be old some day," she said, her young arms across her grandmother's aged shoulders, "like you."

Cap'n Salt Outwits the Wolf

CAROL CARRICK

There's an old seaman everyone in our town calls Cap'n
Salt. The time had come in his life when he felt too old for
the adventure of putting to sea again. Because he loved
the sight of water all around, he bought himself a tiny
island with an abandoned lighthouse on it. With the rest of
his savings he built a cabin as trim as a Yankee sailing
ship.

The Cap'n kept a goat for milk, a sheep for wool, and a
wolf—brought back from his last trip to Alaska—that lay
across his feet in the evening to keep off the chill.

"A wolf!" you say. "Why not a cat or dog? They warm
the feet and make pleasant company too."

Well, you can't expect a man who has traveled the
world many times and more to do things in an ordinary
way. Now can you?

They got on very nicely. The sheep and goat grazed
the tiny meadow and dozed together under the trees. The
Cap'n and the wolf shared good fishing and the comfort of
a fire after supper.

Several times a year the Cap'n rowed over to the
mainland for a few necessities—jam for his breakfast
muffins, cocoa to put in hot milk on winter nights, and
black jelly beans, which were his special weakness.

He always took the wolf with him on these trips. As the
Cap'n put it, "That wolf's been a perfect gentleman up till
now, but he might get the notion to run things his own way
while I'm gone."

145

This was a nice way of saying that the wolf might be curious to see how lamb or goat meat tasted after a steady diet of fish.

One night the Cap'n was awakened by high winds whipping the house and hurling rain against the windows. By morning the sea had flooded the meadow, and the sheep and goat were bleating on the porch to be let in. When the water began to creep under his door, the Cap'n untied the dinghy—now floating in water that covered the dock—and fastened it to the flagpole outside his window.

Hour by hour the water continued to rise, until the Cap'n and his animals were forced up on the roof. Clearly, they would not be safe for long. The waves had grown too high and the current too swift for a crossing to the mainland. The only safe course was to row to the old lighthouse at the other end of the island. The little boat could hold only one passenger besides the Cap'n, so he would have to make three trips.

The Cap'n hauled the sheep into the dinghy, untied the rope that had slid up the flagpole with the rising water, and pushed off.

He was halfway to the lighthouse before he noticed that the wolf was grinning horribly and hungrily at the goat. Although a spunky creature and not at all reluctant to use her sharp little horns, the goat was upset by the storm and terrified of the wolf, who at last had found a chance to sample goat meat. So the goat bleated loudly for the Cap'n to come to her rescue.

The Cap'n and the sheep quickly returned to the roof. After receiving a crack on the nose for his evil thoughts, the wolf climbed meekly into the boat and was rowed away from his two tempting companions.

The Cap'n left the wolf at the lighthouse and went back for another passenger. He tried to push the frightened goat into the boat, which was rocking fearsomely, but the goat stiffened her legs and refused to budge. So the Cap'n seized the sheep before she had a chance to protest, and flopped her into the dinghy.

The Cap'n pulled at the oars with all his strength and was soon at the lighthouse again. The wolf was overjoyed to have company. He pranced about, thumping his tail and rolling his eyes. Suddenly it struck the Cap'n like a blow to the head that he was bringing the wolf another chance at a meal. How could he protect the sheep and still go back and rescue the goat, whose bleating head was all that remained above the water? Cap'n Salt looked at the wolf, and then he looked at the water. And then he knew what to do.

Can you guess what the Cap'n did? Remember, he could take only one animal in the boat at a time, and he couldn't leave the wolf alone with either the goat or the sheep. When you figure out the answer, turn to the next page for Cap'n Salt's solution.

Cap'n Salt's Solution

The Cap'n showed the wits by which he had survived great storms at sea, pirates, shipwrecks, and hostile natives. He quickly traded the wolf for the sheep and rowed back with him to the submerged house. Then he dumped the wolf, took on the goat, who was now very cooperative, and bent his aching back once more to the oars.

With the goat and sheep stowed safely in the lighthouse, the Cap'n pushed off for one last trip. The roof had long since disappeared under the water, and the wolf was dog-paddling furiously. The Cap'n pulled him into the boat, where the wolf shook water all over him. Perhaps this was his way of getting even.

Finally, the storm rolled away, the sun broke out over the island, Cap'n Salt repaired the damage to his house, and everyone was so happy that all was forgiven. Cap'n Salt sat in a rocking chair on his porch and gazed contentedly over the sea, now back in its place. I really am too old to go out looking for adventure, he thought, but I can still handle one when it comes looking for me.

Cluster 4

The Soup Stone

MARIA LEACH

One day a soldier was walking home from the wars and came to a village. The wind was cold; the sky was gray; and the soldier was hungry. He stopped at a house on the edge of the village and asked for something to eat. "We have nothing for ourselves," the people said. So the soldier went on.

He stopped at the next house and asked for something to eat. "We have nothing ourselves," the people said.

"Have you got a big pot?" said the soldier. Yes, they had a big iron pot.

"Have you got water?" he asked. Yes, they had plenty of water.

"Fill the pot with water and put it on the fire," said the soldier, "for I have a soup stone with me."

"A soup stone?" they said. "What is that?"

"It is a stone that makes soup," the soldier said. And they all gathered around to see this wonder.

The woman of the house filled the big pot with water and hung it over the fire. The soldier took a stone from his pocket (it looked like any stone a person might pick up in a road) and tossed it into the pot.

"Now let it boil," he said. So they all sat down to wait for the pot to boil.

"Could you spare a bit of salt for it?" said the soldier.

"Of course," said the woman and pulled out the salt box. The soldier took a fistful of salt and threw it in the pot, for it was a big pot. Then they all sat back to wait.

"A few carrots would taste good in it," said the soldier longingly.

"Oh, we have a few carrots," said the woman and pulled them out from under a bench, where the soldier had been eyeing them. So they threw the carrots in the pot. While the carrots boiled, the soldier told them stories of his adventures.

"A few potatoes would be good, wouldn't they?" said the soldier. "They'd thicken the soup a bit."

"We have a few potatoes," said the oldest girl. "I'll get them." So they put the potatoes in the pot and waited for the soup to boil.

"An onion does give a good flavor," said the soldier.

"Run next door and ask the neighbor for an onion," said the farmer to the smallest son. The child ran out of the house and came back with three onions. So they put the onions in. While they waited, they were cracking jokes and telling tales.

151

"I haven't tasted cabbage since I left my mother's house," the soldier was saying.

"Run out in the garden and pull a cabbage," said the mother. So a small girl ran out and came back with a cabbage. And they put that in the pot.

"It won't be long now," said the soldier.

"Just a little longer," said the woman, stirring the pot with a long ladle.

Just then the oldest son came in. He had been hunting and brought home two rabbits.

"Just what we need for the finishing touch!" cried the soldier, and it was only a matter of minutes before the rabbits were cut up and thrown into the pot.

"Ha!" said the hungry hunter. "The smell of a fine soup."

"The traveler has brought a soup stone," said the farmer to his son, "and he is making soup with it in the pot."

At last the soup was ready, and it was good. There was enough for all; the soldier, the farmer, his wife, the oldest girl, the oldest son, the little girl, and the little son.

"It's a wonderful soup," said the farmer.

"It's a wonderful stone," said the wife.

"It is," said the soldier, "and it will make soup forever if you follow the formula we used today."

So they finished the soup. When the soldier bade them good-by, he gave the woman the stone to pay back the kindness. She protested politely.

"It is nothing," the soldier said and went on his way without the stone. Luckily he found another just before he came to the next village.

The soldier with the soup stone has visited nearly every town in northern Europe. He has made soup in many a small New England village, and occasionally one hears of his travels down South or out West.

The magic of the soup stone ALWAYS WORKS if you follow the formula, though some say the magic lies in the hands it falls into.

Matter, Matter, Everywhere

SEYMOUR SIMON

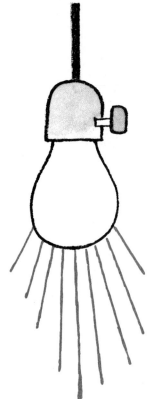

The book you are reading, the chair you are sitting on, the cans in the cabinets, the food in the refrigerator, and the air you breathe are all examples of matter. You yourself are also an example of matter.

However, there are some things around you that are not matter. The light coming to you from the light bulb is not matter. The heat given off by the stove is not matter. The electricity that makes the fan turn is not matter. Light, heat, and electricity are examples of energy.

We say that energy is the ability to do work. Light can make plants grow. Heat changes food from one form to another. Electricity runs machines. There are many different kinds of energy. Everything around you is either matter or energy.

154

Solids

Liquids

Matter comes in three forms: solid, liquid, and gas. This book and a pencil are examples of solids. Water, milk, and cooking oil are examples of liquids. Air, steam, and the gas from a stove are examples of gases. All three forms of matter take up space. All three forms have weight. None of the forms of energy has weight or takes up space. That's how you can tell the difference between matter and energy.

How much bulk something has, or the amount of space it takes up, is called an object's volume. A liter of milk is an example of liquid volume. One hundred grams of sugar is an example of solid volume.

You can use a bunch of marbles, a glass, and some water to find out more about matter. Look at a marble. Try to squeeze it. How would you describe its shape? Can you change its shape easily by squeezing? Solids have a definite shape and volume.

Try to fill a glass completely with marbles. Is the glass really full? Pour some water into the glass. If the glass were full of marbles, could any water fit into it? The water filled the spaces between the marbles. What differences can you see between the solid marbles and the liquid water? We say that liquids have no definite shape. They take the shape of their container.

Do liquids have a definite volume? Take a measuring cup and pour exactly eight ounces of water into a soup

Gases

155

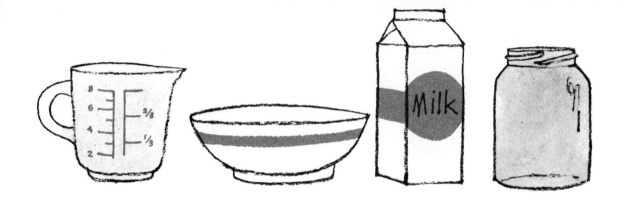

bowl, another eight ounces of water into an empty milk container, and a third eight ounces of water into an empty jar. There is exactly the same volume of water in each of the containers, even though their shapes are different.

You can use a plastic food bag to find out about gases. Blow up the plastic bag and tie it closed. Squeeze the bag into different shapes. You can quickly see that air does not have a definite shape but, like water, takes the shape of its container.

Get an empty glass and a larger, wide-mouthed jar half full of water. Of course the glass is really not empty. It is full of air. You can't see the air, but you can prove it's there. Take a handkerchief and stuff it into the bottom of the glass. Now turn the glass upside down and submerge it in the water in the jar. The water rises only a bit into the glass. It is kept out by the air in the glass. Remove the glass and pull out the handkerchief. It will still be dry.

Turn the glass upside down in the jar of water again and look at it a little more closely. The level of water in the glass rises as you push it deeper. The air in the glass is compressed, which means that it is squeezed into a smaller volume.

Pour any bubbly drink into a glass to see gas expand, or take up more space. Watch the bubbles rising to the top of the glass. They are small at the bottom and larger at the

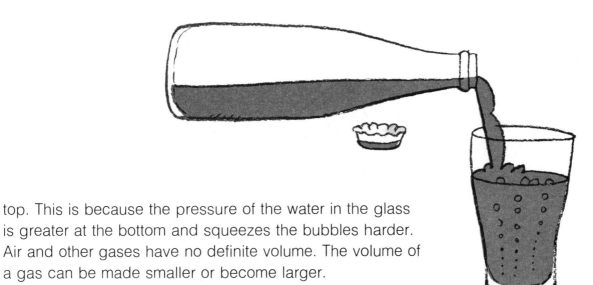

top. This is because the pressure of the water in the glass is greater at the bottom and squeezes the bubbles harder. Air and other gases have no definite volume. The volume of a gas can be made smaller or become larger.

Changing water from one form of matter into another is easy in a kitchen. Ask for permission to boil some water in a teakettle. When the water begins to boil, watch the spout. The cloud that you see disappearing a few inches above the spout is liquid water turning into a gas. The gas is called steam, or water vapor. When water changes into water vapor, we say that it evaporates.

Water left standing in an open glass disappears into the room after a while. It evaporates slowly at room temperature and much more rapidly at higher temperatures. Water vapor is invisible. That's why you can't see it when it goes into the air.

You can make water vapor visible by turning it back into water. Exhale on a cold, glass surface, like a window pane on a cold day. The mist that forms on the glass is made up of tiny drops of water. The cold glass changed the water vapor in your breath into water. When water vapor changes into water, we say that it condenses. Does this help explain why you can see your breath when you are outside on a cold winter day?

If we cool water even more, it freezes into a solid. Ice or

157

snow is water as a solid. Take an ice cube from the freezer compartment of your refrigerator. Place it in a glass and leave it out. After a while it will melt into water, and after a longer while it will evaporate into water vapor. The water vapor in the air outside eventually falls back to the earth's surface as rain or snow. There it evaporates again, and the water cycle continues.

Other substances besides water also change from one form of matter to another. You may have seen pictures of blast furnaces where iron is heated to very high temperatures until it becomes a liquid. Plumbers melt a mixture of lead and tin called solder. The liquid solder flows around the joints of pipes and then cools and hardens to make a tight connection. You can see that the form matter is in depends partly upon its temperature.

Neither water nor iron nor solder changes into a new material when it is heated or cooled. Water is still water and iron is still iron, whether they are solids or liquids or gases. A change from one form of matter to another is called a physical change. During a physical change, a material can change its form or size or shape, but it does not change into a different material.

To see another kind of change you can use a wooden match and a metal pan. Ask permission to light the match and place it in the metal pan. Make sure that there is

nothing near the pan that can catch fire. Without touching it, let the match burn itself out. Compare the burned-out match with a fresh match. How does the wood change after it burns?

When wood or any other material burns, a new kind of material is made. This kind of change is called a chemical change. When a chemical change takes place, the new material has properties that are not the same as the old material.

Chemical changes go on all around us. When steel rusts, it changes into a new material. When someone mixes cake batter and places it in an oven, it changes into a new material. When food rots and decays, it changes into a new material. Can you think of any other chemical changes that go on around you?

Matter may undergo physical changes or chemical changes. But it cannot be destroyed, only changed. In one form or another, matter is everywhere.

Fragrance of Ghosts

JANE EPPINGA

You must believe this story because it is true, and you must not laugh when I say that . . . once upon a time there was an old Indian grandmother who displayed great love and courage. She was a tiny, unimportant old woman with snowy white hair and arms like two brown sticks. Once she had been very lovely, but now, because

she was old and did not wear a scarf on her head like the other women, everyone called her Grandmother White Hair.

She lived a long time ago with her tribe in a desert village. Now, the desert Indians were peaceful, and they farmed the arid land according to the ancient principles taught them by the Good Spirit. They never achieved fame for their bravery like the Apaches or honor for their hunting skills like the Sioux. They were a simple people, who today are known as the Papagoes.

Grandmother White Hair and her husband, Cloud Man, had a beautiful daughter whom they called Morning Light. Life was happy for this family until the day a brave from the faraway village of Hee-ah-kim came with his band of renegades to raid the desert people. This brave, known as Swift-As-The-Four-Winds, was struck by Morning Light's beauty and, to the sorrow of her parents and friends, took her to be his wife and live in Hee-ah-kim.

Grandmother White Hair grieved for Morning Light because she knew only evil could come from the warlike people of Hee-ah-kim. Her one comfort was to go to the foot of Beehive Mountain at sunset and commune with her daughter's spirit. One night she returned home deeply troubled. Grandmother White Hair burned the bread; she burned the beans; and, worst of all, she spilled the precious drinking water.

Cloud Man scolded, "Why did you burn the bread? Why did you burn the beans? Why did you spill the precious drinking water?"

Grandmother White Hair hung her head in shame. Then Cloud Man asked in a gentle voice, "What troubles you, my wife?"

Big tears fell down Grandmother White Hair's wrinkled face. A long time passed before she answered, "Morning Light is in trouble. She needs me."

Cloud Man smiled and said, "Silly woman, there is nothing to fear. Morning Light is all right." Nevertheless, he was disturbed because he loved Grandmother White Hair and Morning Light very much. Moreover, he knew that Grandmother White Hair was usually right about matters of the spirit.

She was even more worried when she returned home from the mountain the next night.

"How is Morning Light?" Cloud Man asked anxiously.

"I could not find her spirit," she replied.

After supper they sat outside and watched the stars. Both were silently remembering the days when Morning Light was a child. At last Grandmother White Hair said, "I am going to Morning Light."

Cloud Man protested, "The journey is long. You do not know the way. You are too old, and even if you did get there, you cannot speak the language of the Hee-ah-kim. It is impossible."

Grandmother White Hair did not want to go against her husband's wishes, so she waited a few days. There were no messages from her daughter's spirit. Then one night she came home and said, "I must go. Morning Light is sick and wants me to get our grandson. She is very weak and couldn't send a message herself, so she sent it with Crow."

Now, everybody knows Crow is an outrageous gossip, and, because he chatters with everyone along the way, it takes him forever to deliver a message.

Cloud Man knew it was useless to protest, so he only said, "May the Good Spirit guide you."

Early the next morning, Grandmother White Hair started on her journey. She had not gone very far when a flock of desert birds joined her. They laughed and called, "Old woman, give us some of your hair for our nests."

"Take whatever you need," she replied.

The birds were surprised that she could understand them. In ancient times all the desert people could

163

communicate with the desert animals, but it was generally thought the art had been lost. Immediately the birds loved this frail old woman, and the story of her ability to speak their language spread to all the desert animals.

Raven protected her when she rested; Dove fed her wild honey when she was hungry; Coyote guided her over the mountains to the village of Hee-ah-kim; and finally, on a moonless night, Jackrabbit took her to the home of Morning Light.

The joy of holding her grandson turned to grief when Morning Light told Grandmother White Hair that the men of Hee-ah-kim intended to teach the boy to live by stealing and killing.

"Mother, take my son back to the desert people where he will learn to be brave and gentle," pleaded Morning Light. "I am too ill to do this myself."

"I will do as you wish, my daughter," promised Grandmother White Hair. And so she kissed Morning Light, put the baby in her basket, and said farewell. Then she made her way out of the village, going quickly and quietly so as not to wake any of the Hee-ah-kim.

Maybe it was because she was weary, or maybe it was the water in her eyes that caused Grandmother White Hair to lose her way soon after she had passed the village boundaries. After several hours of wandering in the mountains around Hee-ah-kim, she cried to the desert animals for help.

Immediately Coyote appeared at her side. Slowly and carefully he led Grandmother White Hair through the mountains. They slept during the day and traveled at night. When they finally emerged onto flat arid land,

Coyote warned, "We must be careful because we are still in the land of the Hee-ah-kim, and they are searching everywhere for your grandson."

Grandmother White Hair became discouraged and wondered if she would ever see her desert people again. While Coyote was searching for food, she cried to the earth for help. The voice of the Good Spirit answered, "You must go on. Do not stop. For the remainder of the journey, rest at night and travel during the day along the washes." Grandmother White Hair took courage from his words, and when Coyote returned, she told him of the Good Spirit's instructions. Together they searched, and eventually they found the beginning of a very shallow wash in the parched land. It gradually became deep enough for Grandmother White Hair to walk between its banks.

Coyote walked along the bank above her, and the birds called out a warning when the Hee-ah-kim approached. Then Grandmother White Hair hid in the thick brush until the animals told her it was safe to proceed.

The Good Spirit was always present with help and encouragement for Grandmother White Hair. Sometimes he came as a gentle breeze and sometimes as a shadow from the clouds passing overhead. The bands of the Hee-ah-kim grew larger and seemed to be everywhere, but the Good Spirit walked with Grandmother White Hair. His footsteps made new and deeper washes.

Then one morning the Hee-ah-kim spied her white hair and came after her. While the Good Spirit sang the Earth song, the banks of the wash closed in, and all the desert birds swarmed in a cloud around Grandmother White Hair. She lifted her grandson high in the air, and the largest of the birds, Eagle, took the child and flew off. When the cloud of birds disappeared, the Good Spirit had transformed Grandmother White Hair into two brown sticklike bones and some white hair. The Hee-ah-kim, frightened by the disappearance of the old woman and the child, returned home. Unused to the ways of the Good Spirit, they could not see or know that Grandmother White Hair's spirit was resting on the cool, soft earth.

In the evening, the Good Spirit returned and wakened her, saying, "Eagle has returned your grandson to the desert people. He is safe, and Cloud Man will raise him to be a good man. And now, because you have been brave and made a great sacrifice, I will grant you one wish for anything you want."

Grandmother White Hair smiled shyly and said, "My wish is very foolish, especially for an old woman."

"Your heart could never contain anything foolish," said the Good Spirit.

Grandmother White Hair hesitated. "I would like to be beautiful again," she said softly, "just for a little while."

"Once every year you will be more beautiful than anything else on earth," said the Good Spirit. "Your unselfish love has brought new life to the earth and so will give rise to a new flower. Its stalk will be brown like your arms and its bud, white like your hair." As he spoke, the Good Spirit gently touched the brown sticklike bones. Where his fingers rested there appeared a soft white bud. It grew large and opened into a beautiful flower.

And so from that time on, for one night each year, this white flower opens up on brown stalks and spreads its fragrance over the desert air. At dawn it dies. For one night each year, Grandmother White Hair is more beautiful than any other living thing. Some call this flower the night-blooming cereus, but the desert people call it Fragrance of Ghosts.

A Mysterious Disappearance

KEITH ROBERTSON

Henry Reed is spending the summer with his aunt and uncle in New Jersey. He is hoping that his friend Midge Glass will help in a summer theater production he is planning. In this chapter from *Henry Reed's Big Show* the two friends share a memorable afternoon.

I went over to Midge's house today to talk about the party I want to have for the kids who might be in my theater group. We didn't get very far. In fact, the whole day has been pretty much a waste of time as far as my show plans are concerned. I'd hardly walked into Midge's yard when she came rushing out the door.

"Hey, Henry, how would you like to go for a ride today?" she asked, all excited.

"Where to?" I asked, because I wasn't much interested in going to some place like a shopping center. My feet hurt whenever I get near a shopping center. Stores have the hardest floors in the world.

"Oh, just around," she said, waving her hand up at the hills. "On horses, I mean."

"Sounds all right," I said.

"Boy, you're enthusiastic!" Midge said.

Girls are funny about horses. When they become horse-crazy they really go off their rockers. I like horses and I like riding, but there are other things that are just as much fun and maybe more. Girls who like horses are like people who coo over every baby they see. They think you're a traitor if you don't think every single one is wonderful. Anyone with any sense knows they aren't. Some babies are ugly and some horses are ornery and some of both are dumb. I could see that Midge was suffering from an attack of horse mania. She's very sensible ordinarily, and we're old friends, so I decided to be nice and play along.

"Well, I haven't got any definite plans for today. A ride would be fun. What's the pitch?" I asked.

"The Gleasons have two horses and they're going away for the weekend. They'd like to have the horses get some exercise and we can ride them all day if we want."

I was about to say that I thought an all-day ride might be a little too much of a good thing, but I didn't get a chance.

"We can make some sandwiches and take them along for lunch," Midge said. "There's some wild country over on Province Line Road. You can't get through with a car. We could eat our lunch someplace in the woods."

That sounded interesting, so I agreed to go. Besides, I could see that Midge really wanted to. Also I wanted to stay on her good side because I'm going to need her help in my theater production. I went home and was back in about fifteen minutes with my sandwiches and a can of orange drink. Midge had a brown canvas knapsack, and we put everything in that.

It turned out the Gleasons lived several miles away, so Mrs. Glass drove us there. "Where are you going to ride?" she asked as we drove up the Gleasons' drive.

"Over toward Hopewell," Midge said.

"Will you be going by the Sillimans'?"

"Near there. We could go if you want us to. Why?"

"I owe Mrs. Silliman five dollars," Mrs. Glass said. "I forgot all about it until just now."

She gave Midge the five dollars, let us out near the barn, and drove off. Midge started fussing with one pocket and then another, deciding where to put the five dollars.

"Why don't you let me carry that," I said. "I'm used to carrying money around, and I've never lost any."

I was just trying to be helpful, but she took it as an insult. "I am quite capable of holding onto five dollars for a few hours," she said.

The horses—a big bay and a pinto—were in their stalls. Both of them were well-fed and quiet looking. I've always been taught that you should be very careful around a horse, especially until you get to know it well. Maybe I was acting extra cautious as I led the bay—whose name was Ginger—out to the post where we were going to saddle them.

169

"Do you know how to ride?" Midge asked suddenly.

"Of course I know how to ride," I said. It was a silly question, so I said, "I've ridden horses all over the world."

This was almost true. I rode several times when we lived in England and probably most often while we lived in Italy. And one time when we were in Sardinia I rode a donkey for an hour or so.

"These are both English saddles," Midge said. "No saddle horn."

"The saddle I used in England happened to be an English saddle," I said, getting a little annoyed. I guess because I hadn't jumped up and down with joy when she suggested going for a ride, she thought I didn't know how to ride or was scared or something.

We cleaned the horses and saddled them and rode off. Ginger wasn't quite as quiet and well behaved as I had expected. It wasn't that he did anything really bad, but he would shy at all sorts of silly things, like a little piece of paper beside the road. I was carrying the knapsack with our lunch over my shoulder, and each time we went faster than a walk, it would bounce up and down. This seemed to scare him, so finally Midge took the lunch.

We rode along back roads for a mile or so until we came to a gate beside a small stream. There was a pasture on both sides of the stream, with clumps of trees scattered around.

"This stretches all the way through to the next road," Midge said. "And there's a gate at the end. I've cut through here several times. It's fun riding along beside the stream."

I got off and opened the gate and then closed it after we were through. Ginger was a big horse and getting back on him wasn't easy, especially since he wasn't too well trained and kept moving each time I got my foot in the stirrup. I had to make about six tries. I felt silly with Midge watching me suspiciously.

Partway through the pasture we came to a beautiful open stretch of smooth green grass. The horses wanted to run, so we let them gallop for quite a distance. When we got to the other end of the pasture I got off again to open the gate onto the road. My comb dropped out of my pocket as I got off, and when I put it back I noticed that my glasses were gone. I wear glasses for reading, but I don't need them all the time. I knew I had put them in my pocket after I had finished saddling Ginger.

"I've lost my glasses someplace," I said.

"We can go back and look for them now or come back this way," Midge suggested.

"I think I'd better go back now," I said. "If I dropped them back on the road, some car might come along and run over them."

At first we were going to go back together, but then we had a better idea. Midge would deliver the five dollars to the Sillimans while I went back to look for my glasses. We agreed to meet farther on up the road, beside a high radio tower.

I rode along slowly, trying to retrace the way we had come. I hadn't gone any distance at all when I saw my brown leather glasses case lying on the grass. It must have bounced out of my pocket while we were galloping. I got off and picked it up, and this time I got back on Ginger on the first try. I gave a shout to Midge, thinking that I could catch up with her and we could ride over to the Sillimans' and back together. She didn't answer. I put Ginger into a gallop, thinking I would ride fast and catch her. We galloped a short distance, but then Ginger dropped back to a trot and I changed my mind. My behind was getting a little tender. So I decided to go on up the road at a nice gentle walk. I knew I would get to the radio tower long before Midge, but I could always get off and take it easy while I waited.

Ginger kept turning toward the stream, and it didn't take much intelligence to figure out that he wanted a drink. I saw a nice shallow spot with a gravelly bottom, so I rode him out into the middle of the stream and let up on the reins, and he promptly put his head down and began to drink. My shoestring had come untied, so I leaned down to tie it while Ginger was busy drinking. That was a foolish thing to do. Something scared Ginger. I don't know whether it was a small fish, a falling leaf, or a bird flying by. It doesn't take much to scare him. I think he likes being scared. He jumped about two feet to one side. I was already leaning way over and I wasn't expecting him to move. I pitched forward and landed face down in the stream.

The water was only about six inches deep. I didn't fall very far, but I banged my nose on a rock on the bottom and I was completely soaked from head to foot. I got to my feet, wiped the water out of my eyes, and looked for Ginger. He had forgotten all about whatever had scared him and was drinking again about three feet from me. I walked up to him and he made no effort to run away.

I led him out of the water and then paused on the bank to decide what to do. Water was dripping from my hair and clothes and squishing in my shoes as I walked. I looked down at my shirt pocket to see if I still had my glasses and saw that my whole shirt was covered with blood.

I put my hand up to my nose and, sure enough, I had a nosebleed. My nose bleeds very easily. All it needs is a little bump and it starts spurting like a fountain. Blood was running down with the water and dripping off my chin. I was wearing a new green-and-white checked sport shirt that Aunt Mabel had given me. If I didn't do something soon I could see it would be a red, green, and white sport shirt.

I was standing near a big clump of bushes, and beyond them, back from the stream, was a small tree. I led Ginger over to the tree and tied him. Then I stripped off my shirt. My pants had blood on them too. The bushes hid me from the road, so I took off my pants also. I took everything out of my pockets and waded out into the stream. Both my shirt and pants were made of material that dries very fast. I guess they don't stain very easily either, because the blood came right out. I pressed the water out of them as well as I could, and spread them out on a couple of the bushes where the wind

and sun would catch them. It was a warm day with a good breeze, and I knew they would be dry in a few minutes.

My nose was still bleeding and blood had run down all over my bare chest. There seems to be only one way I can ever stop a nosebleed, and that is to lie flat on my back and put my head way back. Usually I lie on the bed and let my head hang over the edge. I had to wait for my shirt and pants to get at least a little dry, so I picked a spot upstream where the bank beside the stream was high. I lay down on the grass on my back and let my head hang over the edge of the bank. I closed my eyes and relaxed in the warm sun.

It was nice lying there and I almost went to sleep. I had put my glasses, knife, handkerchief, and watch in a little pile a few feet away. Finally I reached out and looked at my watch and discovered that I had been there more than half an hour. I didn't know how long it might take Midge to get to the Sillimans' and back to the radio tower, but I decided it was time to move. I felt my nose. It had stopped bleeding. I went down to the stream and carefully washed the blood off my face and chest.

My clothes looked much drier than they actually were. However, they weren't too bad, just sort of damp. It took me only a minute to dress. I led Ginger the short distance to the gate, got on, and rode off down the road at a canter.

It was at least two miles to the radio tower, and I kept Ginger at a canter most of the way. Between the sun and the wind, I was practically bone dry by the time we got there. There was no sign of Midge, so I led Ginger around a few minutes to cool him off and then tied him to a tree at the edge of the woods. I was sitting on a nice soft pile of leaves, leaning

back against a big tree, when Midge arrived.

"Find your glasses?" she asked.

"No trouble at all," I said, holding them up. "They bounced out of my pocket while we were galloping in that open stretch near the stream."

"Then you've been waiting for me for a long time," she said.

"Not so long," I said truthfully. "I fooled around at the stream for a while. Got my feet wet too."

"I'm sorry to be so late," she said. "But everything delayed me. When I got there, Mrs. Silliman was on the telephone. Finally, when she quit talking, I was able to give her the five dollars and get started. I decided to take the cross road instead of going back the same way. But they were repairing the road, and I couldn't get this idiot horse to go by that big roller. Maybe if I had insisted, he might have, but I decided the safest thing to do was go back. When I got down by the gate where we came out of that pasture, a car came whizzing up with a woman driving. Behind her was a state trooper in his car. They jumped out and ran through the gate. I decided

to find out what all the excitement was about."

"What happened?" I asked.

"I still don't know," Midge said. "The woman claimed that someone had been murdered."

"Murdered? Where? Near where we were riding?"

"Someplace right beside the stream," Midge said. "It seems she's a bird watcher. She writes books and teaches classes about birds. Anyhow, she was walking along the top of that ridge looking for some kind of rare bird. She came from the same direction as we did. She was looking through her binoculars when she saw a corpse down near the stream. It was the body of a man, and it was all mangled and horrible. The head was hanging over the bank and the face was covered with blood. She thinks his throat had been slit."

I kept a perfectly straight face. I suppose I should have told Midge what had happened, but then I would have got involved in a long explanation. She would never have believed that I fell off Ginger while I was tying my shoelace. I could tell she didn't think I really knew how to ride and she would have thought

176

Ginger had thrown me. If she was going to act so suspicious, it would serve her right to wonder what had happened.

"Did you see this body?" I asked.

"No. We couldn't find it. The woman wasn't exactly certain where she had been, she was so excited. She had hurried all the way back to the other road—you know, where we came in. She had left her car there. She drove to the nearest house and called the police. When they came back they went into the pasture from this end, so maybe that confused her. She claimed she knew roughly where she had seen him, but there was no sign of anyone there. I rode up and down the stream for quite a distance and I couldn't see anything."

"Maybe she was imagining things," I suggested.

"That's what the state trooper suggested. She was furious. She was positive she had seen a bloody body."

"Maybe this body wasn't so dead," I said. "Maybe it got up and walked away. Did she feel its pulse?"

"She wasn't near enough," Midge said. "She said it was so bloody there wasn't any doubt about it. She saw it very clearly with her binoculars. Maybe whoever murdered the man came and took the body away." Midge looked around at the trees. "He could be someplace in the trees right now, burying the body."

"Maybe the wolves ate him," I said. "Which reminds me—let's have a sandwich."

177

"Disgusting!" Midge said. "How can you talk about wolves eating a bloody human body and then in the same breath ask for a sandwich?"

"I'm used to blood," I said, which is quite true, because I've had a lot of nosebleeds. "Besides, my theory is that this woman made up the whole story and no one was killed at all. People will do anything for a little excitement."

Midge dismounted and got out the sandwiches. I noticed that the story about the dead man by the stream didn't seem to bother her appetite either.

"I have a feeling about this summer," Midge said as she finished her sandwich.

"What sort of feeling?" I asked.

"That it's going to be an exciting one," Midge said. "That vanishing body is some sort of sign. Don't you think so?"

My mouth was full, so I just nodded in agreement.

"What do you suppose it's an omen of?" Midge asked. "What does it mean?"

I swallowed. "That things are not always what they seem," I said mysteriously. It was too late to tell her then. She never would have forgiven me.

Echo and Narcissus

OLIVIA COOLIDGE

Narcissus was a beautiful boy with whom many nymphs and maidens fell in love. Among these was the nymph Echo, whom the goddess Hera had enchanted with a strange spell. Because of the spell, Echo could not talk but could only answer by repeating the last words others said.

For a long time, poor Echo followed Narcissus about, unable to speak with him. Then one day as they were hunting, Narcissus became separated from his companions and began to call for them. "Is anybody here?" he shouted.

"Here!" said Echo gladly.

"Come," cried Narcissus.

"Come!" she answered him.

"Here let us meet," called the boy.

"Let us meet," said Echo, but when she appeared, Narcissus cared nothing for her. He was so cold and cruel that the poor nymph crept away and hid herself so that no one would see her misery. She pined and wasted away for love until she faded from sight. Now she is only a voice that still answers with the last words others call.

The gods were angry with Narcissus for his cruel treatment of Echo and because he was unkind to many other girls who were attracted by his beauty. He was also very proud. Therefore, to punish him, they cast a terrible spell on him.

Deep in the woods, there was a clear pool to which no shepherds ever came. No bird or beast or fallen branch ever disturbed its crystal waters. Narcissus came through the woods one day, hot and weary with hunting. He saw the gleaming silver pool with its rim of green grass and stopped to refresh himself.

He threw himself on the bank and put his face down to the water. There he saw a most lovely face upturned to his. He smiled at it in welcome. It smiled lovingly back, but when he bent forward to kiss it, the face broke up into ripples at the touch of his lips. As he sprang back, the face formed again and gazed at him with longing. This time he stretched out one hand cautiously and saw a hand stretched out to meet his. But when his fingers touched the water, there was no one there. In despair Narcissus called to the image, in whispers at first. Then since he saw it speaking, even though he could hear nothing, he called louder and louder. No one answered him except Echo, forlornly repeating his desperate words of love.

For days Narcissus knelt by the pool. Before his eyes he saw the image grow pale and thin, weep tears, stretch out its arms, and look at him. Still he could not hear it and could not touch it, no matter how he tried. At last the gods took pity on his misery and changed him into a flower that we now know as the narcissus.

Shooting Stars

HERBERT S. ZIM

Dusk fell on November 12, 1833, as on any normal autumn evening. But as the night wore on, people noticed shooting stars in the eastern sky. Soon so many were seen that people woke their neighbors to come to share this novel spectacle. Within a few hours the sky was ablaze with thousands of shooting stars. There was a rain of shooting stars, a shower of flashing light, spread over the entire sky—so awesome that people could scarcely believe their eyes. Wherever the night was clear, they marveled at the sight.

181

Many fell on their knees to pray; others feared the world was ending. Church bells were rung. People crowded the streets, afraid to remain at home. Only with the dawn did the flashes of light fade away.

As the sun rose, fear died, and people began to realize that what they had seen was the greatest shower of shooting stars in history. Many showers have appeared since, but none as rich or as brilliant.

You, too, may have seen shooting or falling stars. Perhaps, as one flashed across the sky, a friend has said, "Make a wish." Or you may have heard your grandmother say, as one rapidly faded, "Someone has died." For a long time no one knew what shooting stars really were, so people believed such stories.

Shooting stars are more correctly called meteors. Meteors are only seen when they enter the earth's atmosphere, blaze up, and burn out. Some meteors strike the earth and, when found, are called meteorites; so meteorites are fallen meteors.

Even before the great shower of 1833, astronomers had begun to study meteors. In 1798 two Germans compared observations and estimated that meteors were about 50 miles up—much higher than people had suspected. Until that time, people thought that meteors flashed a few miles away, like lightning. In 1803 a French scientist proved that meteorites were the same as meteors, and did come from outside the earth.

In recent years, scientists have proved that the flashes of light you see at night are caused by bits of iron or stone burning up as they hit the outer edge of the earth's atmosphere at great speed. The particles vary in size, in speed, and in composition. The light flashes they make also vary greatly.

The brightest meteors are called fireballs. These light up the entire sky and are seen for hundreds of miles. The ordinary meteors are much fainter—about as bright as a star. And as with the stars, there are many more faint ones that can only be seen with a telescope.

Most people do not see many meteors, mainly because they are not looking for them. But astronomers who watch the skies see them often. On a clear, average moonless night, you could see about ten meteors an hour, watching only a small fraction of the total sky and seeing only the brightest meteors. But your rate of ten an hour means a million an hour for the entire sky, or about 24 million meteors daily. Of these millions of meteors, 99.9 percent are no bigger than particles of dust.

Though millions of meteorites hit the earth's atmosphere each year, fewer than 2000 have been found and put in museums. Undoubtedly, many more large meteorites have been lost in the ocean or in wilderness areas.

Records over the past century suggest that about twenty-five large meteorites fall in the United States each year. For the whole earth the total is about 2000—an average of five or six a day. Some of these meteorites weigh only a few ounces. The largest one found weighs over sixty tons.

In spite of the number of meteorites which fall, nobody has ever been killed by one. However, in November, 1954, a woman became the first human being known to be struck by one. She was bruised and badly scared. A few meteorites have hit houses. One hit a car. Many have been seen falling, and some have been found within minutes after they struck the earth.

When a meteor enters the thin, upper atmosphere, it is moving so fast that it compresses the air ahead, raising the temperature to several thousand degrees. This heat melts the meteor's surface, changing it to glass if it is a stony meteor, or coating it with black iron oxide if it is an iron meteor. The entire meteor or white-hot fragments burn, and make the bright flash and glowing trail. Occasionally a noise like thunder is reported.

The brightness of meteors depends on their speed (faster ones are usually brighter) and on their weight.

The largest meteorites found are iron ones. Possibly because they are not as strong as iron, stony meteorites break more easily in plunging through the air.

Meteorites striking the earth are buried, shattered, or lost, depending on their size and where they strike. When huge meteorites hit the earth, they may cause explosions as large as atomic bombs. A huge meteor has tremendous energy of motion. On striking the earth this great energy is changed instantly into heat. Heat vaporizes water in the soil and rock so fast that it causes a gigantic steam explosion.

In Arizona, near Winslow, is the best-known meteor crater in the United States. Here a great meteorite or swarm of meteorites struck at least 5000 years ago. The crater is almost circular—4200 feet across and 570 feet deep.

It is a real possibility that both types of meteorites, stony and iron, were produced by the breaking up of a planet as large as the earth. The origin of large meteors may have been the greatest collision of all times within the solar system.

Meteorites are an important challenge to our imagination. Curiosity about flashes of light in the night sky and about odd stones has raised scores of questions. Many are not yet answered, but more and more people have joined the search. For to know the complete story of shooting stars, one must solve the mysteries of the solar system and of our entire universe as well. That is something to think about the next time you see a meteor.

Travel

The railroad track is miles away,
   And the day is loud with voices speaking,
Yet there isn't a train goes by all day
   But I hear its whistles shrieking.

All night there isn't a train goes by,
   Though the night is still for sleep and dreaming
But I see its cinders red on the sky
   And hear its engine steaming.

My heart is warm with the friends I make,
   And better friends I'll not be knowing,
Yet there isn't a train I wouldn't take,
   No matter where it's going.

—Edna St. Vincent Millay

At Home in America

S. CARL HIRSCH

The Virginia mountaintop was Jefferson land. And the fourteen-year-old Thomas knew that someday it would be his own. He knelt on the windy hilltop and gently slipped his father's surveying instruments back into their plush cases.

In the weeks since his father's sudden death, Tom had been feeling frightened and alone. But somehow things seemed better now that he had returned to this mountain crest that he loved, to begin planning his future home.

In his sketchbook, next to the measurements he had just written down, he drew the first pictures of how the place would look. He could almost see the pillars and the round dome of the house, with the orchard and the flower garden. He liked to think of himself inside the house, by the warmth of the fireplace, amid his books and telescopes and music, or with his family and friends. No matter how far he might travel, there would always be home—a safe haven whenever he needed it.

In time, Jefferson did build the house he dreamed of. In fact, he planned every wall and window of it himself. It still stands on the summit at Monticello, a marvel to the thousands who come each year to visit. They find evidence of Thomas Jefferson's genius in each of its thirty-five rooms. He equipped the house with his own clever inventions. To increase the living space he reduced the sizes of stairways and tucked the beds into odd corners. Visitors are amazed at what a pleasing and well-planned home it is. They are amazed, too, at

187

the view. It's as though this man wanted to see all the world through the windows of his study.

Few of us are Thomas Jeffersons. But perhaps we can understand his deep need for a comfortable home. Since the founding of this nation, millions of Americans have expressed this same need in a variety of ways.

Even before European settlers arrived, Native Americans across North America used a wide range of dwellings. Probably the best known of these is the tepee. This was the invention of the Plains Indians, who migrated each season in pursuit of the buffalo herds. The tepee could be quickly set up with a few poles and a hide covering. On moving days, these Indians attached two of the poles to their saddles and piled the folded covering and their belongings on the poles, which were then dragged off by the horses. This was the earliest of America's mobile homes.

Each region of colonial America developed its own styles of housing. Some were designed to overcome special problems of climate. People used whatever raw materials were available to them. Often, too, new Americans built their houses in styles they had known in their homelands.

Old Philadelphia was made up mostly of narrow houses of red brick. New Englanders built over a sturdy framework of heavy oak timbers. Farmers often cleared fieldstone from their cropland and then used the stone to build foundations and chimneys for their farmhouses. Settlers on the frontiers constructed log cabins in the forests and mountains, and sod houses on the prairies. Miners, lumberjacks, and trappers lived in temporary shacks.

By the middle of the nineteenth century the rush of Americans to the cities brought a drastic change in living habits. Seeking jobs, millions crowded into the big urban centers. Immigrants from other lands settled in ghetto neighborhoods. Here they spoke their own languages, followed their old customs, and felt somewhat safe from the prejudice they found in other communities.

Later, former slaves and their children also migrated to the cities in great numbers. They, too, found themselves in crowded ghettos.

Early in the rise of the big cities slum areas appeared, in which families were crammed into small spaces without adequate air, light, and heat, and under terrible sanitary conditions. Such tenement neighborhoods have been described as "the shame of the cities." Even today millions of American families are living in homes that are well below reasonable standards of comfort and health.

Countless families have left the cities for homes in the suburbs. But many others cannot afford to make such a move.

In few countries in the world can we find such contrasts in housing as in America. Many families are encased in the tops of skyscrapers. Some have converted country schoolhouses, storefronts, and even old streetcars into homes. Some people live in houseboats. One unusual kind of dwelling is a dome structure that can be moved from place to place by helicopter.

A remarkable variety of dwellings can also be seen on the nation's highways. Many families move almost constantly from place to place because of their jobs. Some shuttle back and forth each season from the North to the South in order to avoid bad weather.

Patterns of housing in America are constantly changing. Some of this change has to do with changing ways of life. The large, permanent family homestead is less common than it used to be. Families are smaller. Newly married couples may move into a small apartment, buy a home as the family expands, and later return to apartment living when the children are grown up and gone.

The car has also changed the way Americans live. Some people spend more of their waking hours in cars than in their homes. In fact, one young woman who was recently interviewed on a radio program saw no reason for a home. She proclaimed, "I was born in a hospital, educated in a college, courted in an automobile, and married in a church. I eat in drive-ins, stay at motels, shop in shopping centers, and even do my banking through my car window. A home—who needs it? All I really need is a garage!"

Nevertheless, most Americans still cling to a place they call home, or they dream of having one. A home is much more than a place to hang one's hat. People have always tried to build some feeling of home into even the crudest dwellings. Sayings such as "Home Sweet Home" and "There's no place like home" reflect a deep-felt need for a safe haven, no matter how small and simple it may have to be.

Jefferson's Monticello was the home base around which he shaped his entire life. He found his refuge from the tumult of the time where we today find ours—at home.

Pinocchio

CARLO COLLODI

Pinocchio is an unusual wooden puppet who wants more than anything to be a real boy. A good fairy has promised that his wish will be granted if he can only stay out of trouble. This isn't easy for Pinocchio, however, and he has now fallen into bad company again. His friend Lampwick has persuaded Pinocchio to come with him to the city of Playland, where boys play all day and never have to read books or go to school.

As soon as they got inside the city, Lampwick and the other boys hurried to join the rest of the children. Very soon they became excellent friends. Who could be happier or more contented than they?

With continual games and all sorts of pastimes, hours, days, and weeks passed like lightning. "Oh, what a beautiful life!" shouted Pinocchio every time he met Lampwick.

"Do you at last see that I was right?" answered Lampwick. "And to think you didn't want to come! To think you intended wasting your time in studying! If you are free today from nasty books and schools, you owe it to me, to my advice, to my insistence. It's only a real friend who would show such kindness."

"Yes, that's true, Lampwick! If today I am a really happy boy, I owe it all to you. And do you know what the schoolmaster used to say to me about you? He always said, 'Don't have anything to do with that good-for-nothing Lampwick. He is a very bad boy and will lead you into some trouble.' "

"Poor old master!" said the other, shaking his head. "I know that he didn't like me and spoke ill of me. But I have a generous soul, and with pleasure I forgive him."

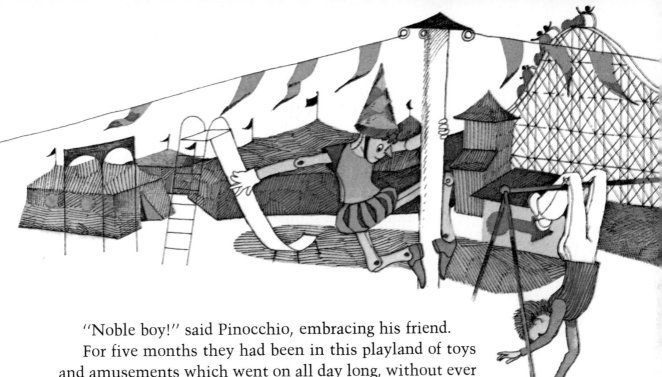

"Noble boy!" said Pinocchio, embracing his friend.

For five months they had been in this playland of toys and amusements which went on all day long, without ever seeing a book or even the outside of a school. Then Pinocchio, upon awaking one morning, had a very unpleasant surprise and lost his good spirits.

And what was this surprise? I shall tell you, my dear readers. The surprise was that Pinocchio, when he woke up, scratched his head; and while doing so he noticed . . . Can you make any guess as to what he noticed?

He noticed, to his great amazement, that his ears had grown several inches.

You must know that puppets from their birth have very small ears, so small in fact that they are invisible to the naked eye. So you can imagine how surprised Pinocchio was when he noticed that his ears had grown so long during the night that they looked like two brooms.

He hurried to find a mirror so that he might see himself. But he could not find one. So he filled his wash basin with water, looked into it, and saw what he had been hoping never to see. He saw himself decorated with a magnificent pair of donkey's ears.

193

Can you imagine poor Pinocchio's sorrow, shame, and despair?

He began to cry and scream and beat his head against the wall, but the more he cried, the longer his ears grew. Then they became hairy at the top.

A charming little squirrel that lived on the floor above him, hearing his loud cries, came down to see what was the matter. Seeing the puppet in such a state, she asked earnestly, "What's happened to you, my dear neighbor?"

"I am sick, dear squirrel. I am very sick—and of such an awful disease. Do you know how to count a pulse?"

"Yes, I think so."

"Then will you please see if I have a fever?"

The squirrel put her right forepaw on Pinocchio's pulse and then said with a sigh, "My friend, I am very sorry, but I have bad news for you."

"What is it?"

"You have a very dangerous fever."

"What kind of fever is it?"

"Donkey fever."

"I never heard of such a fever!" said the puppet, though he knew well what she meant.

"Then I shall explain it to you," answered the squirrel, "for you must know that in a few hours you will no longer be a puppet or a boy."

"What will I be?"

"In a few hours you will be a real donkey, like those that draw carts or carry cabbages and vegetables to the market."

"Oh, poor me! Poor me!" cried Pinocchio, seizing his ears with his hands and pulling and jerking them, as if they belonged to somebody else.

194

"My dear lad," said the squirrel, wishing to console him.

"You can't do anything. It is your destiny. For it is written in the decrees above that lazy children who dislike books, schools, and masters and who spend their time with toys, games, and amusements, must end up, sooner or later, becoming little donkeys."

"Is that really true?" sobbed Pinocchio.

"It is, unhappily. It's no use crying now. You should have thought of that before it was too late."

"But it's not my fault. Believe me, little squirrel, it's all Lampwick's fault!"

"Who is Lampwick?"

"One of my schoolmates. I wanted to go home; I wanted to be good; I wanted to study and never do any mischief. But Lampwick said, 'Why should you bother about studying? Why do you want to go to school? Instead, come with me to Playland. There we shall never study. We shall only play from morning till evening and always be happy!' "

"Why did you listen to that false friend—to that bad companion?"

"Because . . . because, dear little squirrel, I am a heartless puppet with no sense. Oh, if I had had just a little bit of heart, I'd never have left that kind fairy who loved me as a mother and who had done so much for me! And now I could be a real boy, like the others, instead of a puppet! Oh, if I meet Lampwick, he'll get it! I'll fix him!"

He wanted to leave the room. But at the door he remembered his ears, and he was ashamed to show them. So he took a large cotton cap and pulled it over his head, right down to his nose.

Then he went out and looked for Lampwick. He searched the streets, the squares, the theaters, everywhere, but he could not find him. He turned to everyone he met, but no

one had seen him. At last he went to Lampwick's house and knocked at the door.

"Who's there?" asked Lampwick from inside.

"Pinocchio," said the puppet.

"Just a minute, and I'll let you in."

After a long time—at least half an hour—the door was opened. Imagine Pinocchio's surprise when he went in and found that his friend Lampwick wore on his head a great cotton cap which came down over the end of his nose.

Seeing that, Pinocchio felt somewhat better, and he said to himself, "Perhaps he has the same sickness as I have. Can it be possible that he, too, has the donkey fever?"

He pretended not to see anything and said, smiling, "How are you, my dear Lampwick?"

"Very well. As well as a mouse in a Parmesan cheese."

"Do you really mean it?"

"I have no reason to tell you a lie."

"Excuse me, my friend, but then why do you wear a cap that covers your ears?"

"The doctor ordered it, because I've hurt my knee. And you, dear puppet, why do you wear a cotton cap down over your nose?"

"The doctor prescribed it, because I hurt my leg."

"Oh, poor Pinocchio!"

"Oh, poor Lampwick!"

They kept silent for a long while, but the two friends looked knowingly at each other.

At last the puppet said, in a sweet voice full of persuasion, "Just to satisfy my curiosity, dear Lampwick, have you ever had any trouble with your ears?"

"Never! And you?"

"Never! Except that one of my ears was aching this morning."

"Yes, so was mine," said Lampwick.

"Yours, too? Which one aches?"

"Both of them. And yours?"

"Both of them. Do you think we have the same sickness?" asked Pinocchio.

"I'm afraid we do," answered Lampwick.

"Will you do me a favor, Lampwick?"

"Yes, with the greatest pleasure."

"Will you let me see your ears?"

"Why not? But first I'd like to see yours, dear Pinocchio."

"No, you be the first."

"No, dear fellow. You first, and then I'll show mine."

"Well," said the puppet, "let us agree like good friends."

"What to?"

"We'll take off our caps at the same time. Agreed?"

"Agreed."

"Then, ready!" And Pinocchio began to count in a loud voice, "One! Two! Three!"

197

At "Three!" they took off their caps and threw them in the air.

And then something happened that sounds unbelievable; yet it was true. When Pinocchio and Lampwick saw that the same misfortune had befallen them both, instead of being ashamed and despairing, they tried to wag their long ears and finished by laughing at each other.

They laughed and laughed until they nearly exploded.

But suddenly Lampwick stopped laughing. He staggered and grew pale as he spoke to his friend, "Help, help, Pinocchio!"

"What's the trouble?"

"Alas! I can't stand up straight."

"Neither can I," cried Pinocchio, tottering and weeping.

While talking, they bent down on all fours and started running round the room on their hands and feet. As they ran, their hands became hoofs, their faces grew as long as muzzles, and their backs were covered by light gray hair with black spots.

But the most dreadful and the most humiliating moment for those two miserable boys was when they felt their tails growing. Overcome by shame and sorrow, they began to cry over their fate.

Oh, if they had only kept quiet! Instead of sighs, they brayed like donkeys. Yes, both together in chorus, they brayed loudly.

Meanwhile somebody knocked at the door, and a voice shouted, "Open the door! I am the driver who brought you here. Open at once, or it will be worse for you!"

They did not open the door, so the little man kicked it open and addressed Pinocchio and Lampwick with his usual laugh. "Hurrah for you! You brayed very well. I recognized your voices at once. And now, here I am."

At these words the two donkeys became silent, their heads hanging down and their tails between their legs.

At first the little man stroked and patted them. Then drawing forth a currycomb, he combed them well. When they were shiny so that he could see his face in them, he bridled them and took them to market, hoping to sell them at a profit.

Indeed, buyers were not lacking. Lampwick was sold to a farmer whose donkey had died the day before. And Pinocchio was bought by the manager of a company of clowns and ropewalkers, who intended teaching him to jump and dance, together with the other animals belonging to the company.

Now you can see what a fine business the little man carried on. He was a cruel monster, seemingly all milk and honey, going round the world with his coach. By promises and flattery he collected all the children who did not like their books and did not want to go to school. When his coach was full, he carried the children off to Playland, so that they might spend their time playing and amusing themselves. When these poor children, from endless playing and lack of studying, became so many donkeys, he took them to market and sold them happily. In a few years, by this means, he earned a lot of money and became a millionaire.

And because he had abandoned his studies and had not listened to the kind fairy's advice, Pinocchio had become not a boy, but a donkey.

Crystals

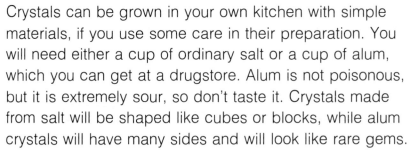

JOHN WAUGH

Crystals can be grown in your own kitchen with simple materials, if you use some care in their preparation. You will need either a cup of ordinary salt or a cup of alum, which you can get at a drugstore. Alum is not poisonous, but it is extremely sour, so don't taste it. Crystals made from salt will be shaped like cubes or blocks, while alum crystals will have many sides and will look like rare gems.

Put about two cups of water in a small pot and heat it on the stove over a low flame. Gradually add the salt or alum and stir occasionally. You want all the salt or alum to dissolve in as little water as possible. If it doesn't all dissolve after a few minutes, add more water a little at a time until it does.

After the liquid has cooled, pour it into a clean bowl. Cover the bowl with a piece of cloth in such a way that the cloth doesn't touch the water. The cloth will prevent the water from evaporating too quickly into the air. Put the bowl in a place where no one will disturb it.

As the water slowly evaporates, crystals of salt or alum will form on the sides and bottom of the bowl. The crystals will be hard to see at first. But check the bowl carefully every day and select the best-formed crystal. Remove the others with a spoon. Leave the best crystal in the water, turning it occasionally so that it doesn't become flat where it rests on the bottom of the bowl. If smaller crystals begin to form on the one you have chosen to let grow, knock them off with a sharp-pointed knife and scoop them out of the bowl.

200

Check your crystal, turn it, and scoop out other crystals twice a day. Don't forget to cover the bowl afterward. The water in the bowl is evaporating into the air, leaving behind the salt or alum. Because you are continually removing all crystals except one, the salt or alum grows mainly on this single crystal, making it bigger and bigger.

When enough water has evaporated to leave the top of your crystal uncovered, you may want to add more liquid so the crystal will continue to grow. Do not add plain water; it will dissolve the crystal. Instead, repeat the first part of this experiment, using more salt or alum, more water, and a second bowl. Don't cover the second bowl; let it sit until crystals begin to form on the bottom. Then pour the liquid from the second bowl into the first bowl. Cover the first bowl again and continue to scoop out small crystals when you turn the big crystal.

When your crystal has grown as large as you want it, take it out and dry it. Crystals of salt may appear slightly cloudy, but crystals of alum will be absolutely clear and will sparkle like precious gems.

If you have a microscope or a strong magnifying glass, look at some grains of salt from a salt shaker or at some of the alum grains you bought. Now look at the crystal you have grown. Can you tell by the shape of your crystal what it is made of?

Crystals develop in nature in a similar manner to the ones you grew in your kitchen. Gather several different rocks from outside and examine them. You should be able to see tiny crystals of all shapes and colors. Just as in your experiment, the bigger the crystals, the longer it took them to grow.

201

Have You Thanked
A Green Plant Today
(Bumper Sticker)

Thank you, thank you, lovely plant,
Eye-delighting oxidant.
You gratify the eye, and then,
To top it off, make oxygen.
You beautify, and then, to boot
(Oh lungs, rejoice) you depollute,
Thank you for this twofold bliss
Wrought by photosynthesis.
   (Now I hereby bequeath to you
   A life supply of CO_2.)

—Don Anderson

202

The Hand of Friendship

LOUISA R. SHOTWELL

Everybody in the entire school knew Daisy Gonzalez, alias Spook.
She was notorious. She was always making faces and scaring people.
And she was usually in trouble for playing hooky or disrupting a
class. Most days she could be seen sitting outside the office of Mrs.
Rostock, the principal, waiting to be disciplined. Everyone,
including Magdalena Mendez, kept out of Spook's way.

Then Spook was transferred into Room 6-310, and Mrs. Rostock
asked Magdalena to befriend her. Magdalena soon discovered that
Spook was bright and not as tough as she seemed. As this story
begins, Spook and Magdalena are just returning from the library.
They had gone there to find Miss Lilley, an elderly friend of Spook's.
Miss Lilley had helped convince Magdalena to have her long braids
cut off.

At home, Spook, not waiting to be asked, tagged
along inside and up the stairs. Magdalena was glad for
her company. But one thing was certain; Spook had
better be gone by the time Nani came home. Even the
new Spook was still wild enough to horrify Nani. She
was terribly dirty and her untamed hair shot up and out
like a nest of snakes gone wild.

"Smells good in here," Spook said, sniffing.

Nani's herbs hung in bunches along the wall. The
kitchen looked orderly as always, thanks to Nani, and
inviting too. It was a comfortable room.

Spook walked around, examining things. She pointed
to the portrait over the refrigerator. "That man's too old
to be your father."

"It's my Great-grandfather Mendez. He's been dead for
years."

"How long? He doesn't look dead."

203

"I don't remember. I never saw him. I think he was born about a hundred years ago. I know he was four years old when the Americans landed in Puerto Rico."

"July 25, 1898."

"That's right! How did you know?"

"Oh, I know a few things. I learned that one from Mr. Cassidy before I disrupted him. He showed us a picture some artist painted of American soldiers scrambling up onto the dock out of little white boats. That was at Guánica."

"Great-grandfather Mendez was there!"

"What was he doing there? I thought you said he was only four years old."

"He was there because that's where he belonged. He lived there. Guánica's close to Ponce, where I was born."

"I was born in Spanish Harlem. We moved to Brooklyn almost right away, so I don't remember it."

"I can tell you a story about Great-grandfather Mendez. It's true. Do you want to hear it?" Magdalena had learned this story from Nani and loved it.

"I don't care. Not specially. Yes, I do. What is it?"

"Well, he was playing on the beach with his pet goat when the Americans came, and he saw one soldier who looked thirsty, so he milked his goat into a gourd and gave it to the soldier. The American soldier drank the goat's milk all up and gave back the gourd, but my great-grandfather would not take it! He put his hands behind his back and he said, 'My gourd is your gourd.' Just the way he'd heard his mother say to company, 'My house is your house.' "

"*Mi casa es su casa.* Cute! He must have been a bright kid. Then what? Did the American soldier understand Spanish?"

"I never thought about that. Anyway, Great-grandfather Mendez ran home and told his mother what he'd done, so that's how we know it's a true story."

"Magdalena! You could write about that for The Purple Pen of 6-310. Miss Killian said we could write about somebody in our family. If I wrote about anybody in my family, she'd whack me for making up bad things. If I made it real, she would. So where's your father?"

"He's a seaman. He's on his way around the world. Today he might be in Singapore. I'm not sure. It could be Manila."

"Where's your mother?"

"Mami's dead. That's why Nani came."

"I shouldn't think your mother was old enough to die, but I suppose it can happen to anybody. My little brother Eustaquio died and he was only three. He had asthma. I still have two brothers left and a sister, all little kids and they're brats. Are they ever! Always grabbing things. The one I really liked was Eustaquio. How about your brothers and sisters?"

"I'm the only one."

"You're not! I never heard of such a thing. You and your grandmother rattling around this great big palace of a place all by yourselves? Must be nice."

Spook wandered some more, touching everything. She lifted up the wooden cover that made a table out of the bathtub.

"Whee! If I had a tub all convenient like this, I'd take a bath every day."

"I do."

"You do not."

"I do too." Magdalena stifled a giggle.

"I don't believe it."

"Well, I do."

"You care if I take one now?"

"Take a bath? Do you want to?"

"Yes, I want to, but I'm not wild about having your grandmother catch me in her bathtub. How do these things work? Never mind, I get it." The water gushed forth. "How do you make the water stay in?"

The drain was operated by a plunger on top of a pipe sticking up from the floor outside the tub. Magdalena pushed the plunger. The tub began to fill. She glanced at the clock. Not quite twenty minutes of five. Nani never came home before five.

Magdalena produced soap and sponge.

"Honest, can I?" Spook asked. "Do you mean it?"

"You said you wanted to. I'm not making you."

"Watch me!" Spook undressed, flinging her clothes in various directions.

The water crept up and up. Magdalena turned off the faucets.

Spook plunged in. "Help! I'm scalding!"

"No, you're not. It'll feel all right in a minute."

Spook recovered and began to scrub, gingerly at first and then with more and more energy. All in all, she performed a thorough job, except for one thing.

"You forgot your ears."

"I did not. Yes, I guess I did."

At last Spook lay back and closed her eyes. "I could fall asleep easy. I think I'll stay right here all night. You really have it made, Magdalena, living in this nice place with nobody to bother you except your grandmother." She opened her eyes. "You never told me if your grandmother was mad because you had your braids cut off."

Magdalena did not answer. She walked jerkily around the room. She collected Spook's garments absentmindedly, as if her thoughts were light years away. All of a sudden she dropped the clothes in a heap on the floor, dragged the step stool over close to the tub, and sat, elbows on her knees and chin resting on her hands.

"Spook, do you think I was bewitched?"

Spook snorted. "What gave you that crazy idea?"

"It's not crazy. Nani said I was." Magdalena reached inside her dress and drew out a small bag. "She makes me wear this. Night and day it has to touch my skin."

"What's in it?"

"Angelica. To fend off witches. I was going to watch it work this afternoon, only she wasn't there."

"Who wasn't there?"

"Miss Lilley. In the library. Miss Lilley wasn't there."

Spook sat up. "What's Miss Lilley got to do with it?"

"I had to know if she's a witch. If she is, the angelica bag would fend her off. Then I'd know for sure."

"Miss Lilley's no witch. You didn't have to go wearing a silly bag to find that out. You could have asked me."

"But do you know? How can you tell? She looks like one. She sounds like one. If she's not a witch, why is her talk so queer? Why does she wear a pumpkin hat?"

"Don't you dare say that! Miss Lilley's my friend!"

"Yes, she's your friend and you're lucky she is. You're lucky, Spook! Don't you see? Miss Lilley bewitched me, and she put a spell on you, too—a good spell! Because she's your friend!"

"Miss Lilley did not put a spell on me!"

"She did, she did! Spook, she's changed you."

"Magdalena, stop it. What ails you? Nobody changed me. I'm the same as I always was."

"Oh, no you're not. You're different."

"How am I different?"

"How? Why all kinds of ways. You don't play hooky; you don't jump out and scare people; you don't even make faces any more."

"Oh, I don't, don't I? How's this?"

Magdalena never saw whatever masterpiece of a face Spook might have produced. Spook never made it. Instead she gripped the rim of the tub on either side and spoke in Spanish. "I'm just leaving."

Magdalena did not need to turn her head. Nani's presence in the room wrapped itself around her like a cloak.

209

"Stay there!" Nani tossed her coat aside and crossed the room to the bathtub. She peered in.

Magdalena cried out.

"Nani, you can't scold her! You mustn't! Her name is Daisy Gonzalez. She's my friend."

"Friend? Enemy? So! She thinks to leave before she cleans my tub? It is necessary she think again."

Nani pushed the plunger. Slowly, slowly, the water sank, gurgle gurgle, until with a dying glunk the last of the liquid went down the drain. The dirt stayed behind.

Nani turned on both faucets. She pulled Spook to her feet and rinsed her off from head to toe. She pushed her down and shampooed the snaky hair. She bundled it in a towel. Only then did she allow Spook to climb out of the tub.

Nani pointed to the low shelf that held the scouring powder and scrub brush. "Use them," she ordered.

Spook reached for powder and brush and went to work. The operation on the tub took several minutes, during which Nani inspected the untidy heap of garments on the floor. One by one she dropped them in a bucket of suds. When Spook finished her chore, her clothes lay in the pail, soaking.

"I can't go home in a towel," said Spook.

At Nani's bidding, Magdalena brought out some clothes of her own for Spook. The dress she found was one Nani had made for her last summer. It was light blue with large white polka dots.

Spook's lips parted. "Christmas! Can I wear that?"

"Why not?" said Nani. "If it fits."

Magdalena had always felt babyish in that dress, but now, with Spook inside it and the addition of a wide white belt, it took on shape and character. Its color suited Spook, brightening her eyes and making her skin look creamy. Her hair, partly dry and no longer snaky, made a becoming frame for her face.

Nani adjusted the belt. She straightened the skirt, gave the dress some final pats, and led Spook to the mirror beside the door.

Nani said, "Behold!"

Spook stared at her reflection. She gazed and gazed as if she were seeing herself for the first time and not believing what she saw.

Magdalena hardly believed it either.

"Why, Spook!" she said. "Spook, you're beautiful!"

Spook's face puckered. Out of her throat came a croaky sound. It couldn't, it could not be that Spook was going to cry. But Spook did not cry. She spat, straight at her image in the mirror. The spit hit the glass like a bullet.

Spook snatched her coat and fled, slamming the door behind her. They could hear her thundering down the stairs.

Surprisingly, Nani had shown neither shock nor anger at Spook for her conduct, nor at Magdalena for letting Spook take a bath.

Oh, Nani had been furious, indeed she had, but not at Spook or Magdalena. The one she was enraged at was somebody she had never seen.

"Such neglect!" she spluttered. "Animals do better. The woman is a monster!"

"Who, Nani? What woman?"

"Who? Who? The mother of that child, that is who!"

"Why, that's what Mrs. Rostock said! Not exactly, but she said Spook's home life was dismal. That must be what she meant," and Magdalena explained to Nani about Mrs. Rostock's request and the hand of friendship. "Spook is the girl Mrs. Rostock asked me to be nice to."

"Ah! Mrs. Rostock. The principal. A wise woman. The child begs for friendship! Ah, how she begs."

"Spook does not beg! She didn't beg to take a bath; it was just that I could tell how badly she wanted to, so I let her. She didn't beg to do it. Spook doesn't beg for anything."

"She has pride, that one. In her own way she begs, with pride. Magdalena, do not disappoint her."

"I won't, Nani. How could I? She's my friend. Only I do not understand what made her do that awful thing in the mirror, right when she'd become all of a sudden beautiful."

"I understand," said Nani.

"You do?"

This made no sense whatever. Nani, announcing that she understood the extraordinary behavior of Spook Gonzalez!

Nani repeated herself. "*Si, si*, I understand, *absolutamente*. The child is like a small colt, untrained. She feels to do a thing and *pronto* she does it. She feels to spit and *pronto* she spits!" And Nani's anger at Mrs. Gonzalez spent itself in a gale of laughter at the recollection of Spook's act.

The next night Nani inquired at once about the girl who took the bath and seemed not in the least surprised when Magdalena said, "She won't speak to me, Nani. She won't even look at me. I can't get near her."

"*Naturalmente*. The child is shy."

"Shy! Oh, Nani! Spook is the most unshy girl I ever met."

"Oftentimes, Magdalena, it is the bold-acting ones who are the most shy. This one feels shame for what she did in the mirror. It is a hard thing to say one is sorry. She may never say it, but when she is ready once more for friendship, be sure you are ready too."

"I'm ready now," said Magdalena.

It was that night that Magdalena had the telephone call.

Sometime after nine o'clock she was finishing her homework when Cruz Candelario banged on the door and yelled for her to come quick, she was wanted on the hall phone.

"Who is it?" she asked, opening the door. "Did they say?"

Cruz was a third-grader and a real monkey. "Some boy friend or other," he told her, looking wicked.

"Magdalena! Is this a boy?" Nani's voice was stern.

"I don't know, Nani." Magdalena sped to answer the call before Nani could ask anything more.

"Magdalena?"

This was no boy. It was Spook Gonzalez. Cruz truly was a monkey.

"Spook! What's the matter?"

"Does something have to be the matter? Can't I call you up if I want to?"

"You never did before."

"I never wanted to before. So before was before and now is now, and I want to talk to you."

"What about?"

"Nothing special. Anything. I went to bed and couldn't sleep, so here I am."

"Where are you?"

"Out on the street in a booth. I had to walk six blocks till I came to one that works."

"Six blocks! All by yourself at night? Did your mother let you go?"

"She'd smack me if she knew. Magdalena, I heard what you said today. I heard you tell Snippety Sue Webster to shut up when she said something bad about me."

"That was awful."

"It was great." Pause. "Magdalena?"

"I'm listening."

"Are you still my friend?"

"You know I am."

"For sure and forever?"

"Of course!"

"No matter what?"

"No matter what."

An audible sigh. Another pause, longer than the first, and then, "Here's another thing."

A click signaled that time was running out on Spook's dime.

"Hurry up, Spook. What's the other thing?"

"The other thing is," Spook said, "I wish I wasn't such a stinker." And the line went dead.

214

Cluster 5

Meet the Computer

BRUCE LEWIS

People today use computers in supermarkets and hospitals and airports, with scientific research and at the launching sites of rockets headed for the moon. Computers are a part of our everyday life, and we have really only begun to use these marvelous machines. But just what is a computer?

A computer is a complicated electronic machine that works with numbers. It is run by electricity and is filled with wires, connectors, switches, and electronic devices. It uses these to add, subtract, multiply, and divide—so quickly that each step may take as little as a billionth of a second! But a computer is still just a machine—and usually a rather modest-looking one at that. There are computer systems that fill whole rooms, and there are computers that are no bigger than a desk. Many are even smaller.

216

Electronic machines are all around us. A television set, a transistor radio, and an amplifier in a record player are all different kinds of electronic machines. But while these machines and a computer may use the same kinds of parts, a computer does its job in a different way. It has more in common with two machines that are not electronic at all—a washing machine and a dishwasher.

Both a washing machine and a dishwasher do a certain kind of job in a certain order. First, you load them with something to work on—clothes or dishes. Next, you tell them what to do. You set the timer or push the buttons for the kind of wash you want. Then you start them, and they follow your instructions one at a time—wash, rinse, spin, and so on. They are mechanical servants that follow your orders and work for you.

A computer is an electronic servant. Like the washing machine and the dishwasher, the computer must be given something to work on. It will follow instructions and solve problems—but only if people tell it what to do. Of course, a computer does not work with clothes or dishes. It works with numbers.

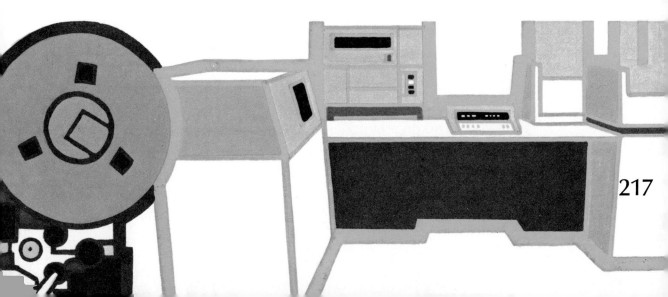

To understand the way a computer works with numbers, think of a light bulb with a switch that turns it on or off. Now if you make a rule that the light bulb stands for *one* when it is on, and for *nothing*, or zero, when it is off, you will have a kind of electrical counter. You can switch it on for one and off for zero.

This is the way computers use electricity to stand for numbers. But instead of light bulbs, computers today use electronic switches called transistors that can be switched on and off. Most of today's computer transistors are so small that they can be seen only through a powerful microscope. These tiny switches are the computer's decision makers. They enable the computer to tell the difference between "on" and "off"—or "yes" and "no." When they are grouped together, the "ons" and "offs" make up a number code that can be used for counting and working with numbers.

Inside a computer there can be many thousands of these tiny electronic counters. Because the counters are like switches they stay the way they are set until the computer is told to change them. Setting them to stand for a number is like putting the number away until it is needed. For this reason, the number is said to be put in *storage*.

Other parts of the computer are used to *process* the numbers—to add, subtract, multiply, or divide them. Processing means moving the numbers around in storage so that the computer can work with them and solve problems.

The control panel, or *operator's console*, is an important part of the computer, too. It is usually on the front of the machine, where you find the buttons and dials and flashing lights. The operator uses it to find out and control what is going on inside the computer.

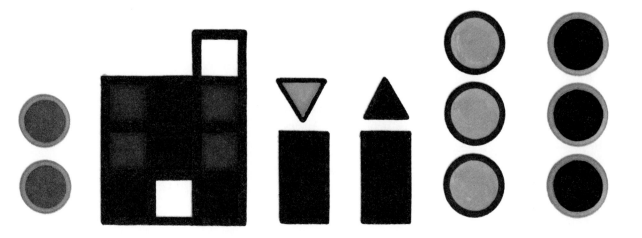

In any computer that solves problems for people there are three different jobs being done—*input*, *processing*, and *output*. These are the three parts of a *computer system*. If we want the computer to process numbers for us, we must have a way to put the numbers into the computer. And we must have a way to get the computer's answers out when it is finished processing them. These things are done with input and output machines.

Input machines are translating machines that change our number language into the electronic number language of the computer. Output machines do just the opposite. After the computer has finished its processing, output machines change computer language to human language so that we can understand and use the work the computer has done.

Who decides on the kinds of input and output and processing? The choice is up to the people who are using the computer. Without people to tell it what to do, the

biggest computer system in the world would be helpless. The people who use it must spell out every single detail of the job they want it to do. They must write instructions that tell the computer what things it needs for processing, where to get them, and what to do with them. These instructions are called a *computer program*. The people who write the instructions are called *programmers*.

Computer programs are often complicated, because they contain a great many instructions. But the instructions themselves are usually simple. Sometimes they can even be written in everyday language. Most important, all the instructions in a program must be correct, so that the computer will do exactly the same things every time. If some of the instructions are wrong, the computer will carry them out anyway, because it can only do what it is told to do. Then all its answers will be wrong, and the programmers must test their programs again and again until all the wrong instructions are found and corrected.

With all the things computers can do, you might think you could never do anything better than a computer. But you can. Every day, you do something that is a lot more complicated than anything a computer will ever do. You think. A computer can't. Not even the biggest, most complicated, most impressive-looking one. You can paint a picture, write a book, or compose a song. You can enjoy pictures and books and songs. A computer can't. In fact, a computer can't do anything at all without a program of instructions written by a human being just like you. But with the right instructions and programs and people, a computer can be a marvelous and powerful tool.

McBroom the Rainmaker

SID FLEISCHMAN

I dislike telling you this, but some folks have no regard for the truth. A stranger claims he was riding a mule past our wonderful one-acre farm and was attacked by woodpeckers.

Well, there's no truth to that. No, indeed! Those weren't woodpeckers. They were common prairie mosquitoes, small ones at that.

Why, skeeters grow so large out here that everybody uses chicken wire for mosquito netting. But I'm not going to say an unkind word about those zing-zanging, hot-tempered, needle-nosed creatures. They rescued our farm from ruin. That was during the Big Drought of last year.

Dry? Merciful powers! Our young'uns found some tadpoles and had to teach them to swim. It hadn't rained for so long those tadpoles had never seen water.

That's the sworn truth, as certain as my name's Josh McBroom. Why, I'd as soon grab a skunk by the tail as tell a falsehood.

Now, I'd best creep up on the story about the Big Drought the way it crept up on us. I remember we did our spring plowing, as usual, and the skeeters hatched out, as usual. The bloodsucking rapscallions could be mighty pesky, but we'd learned to distract them.

221

"Willjillhesterchesterpeterpollytimtommarylarry-andlittleclarinda!" I called out. "I hear the whine of gallinippers. We'd better put in a patch of beets."

Once the beets were up, the thirsty skeeters stuck in their long beaks like straws. Didn't they feast though! They drained out the red juice; the beets turned white; and we harvested them as turnips.

The first sign of a dry spell was when our clocks began running slow. I don't mean the store-bought kind. No one can predict the weather with a tin timepiece. We grew our own clocks on the farm—vegetable clocks.

Now, I'll admit that may be hard to believe, but not if you understand the remarkable nature of our topsoil. Rich? Glory be! Anything would grow in it—lickety-bang. Three or four crops a day until the confounded Big Dry came along.

Of course, we didn't grow clocks with gears and springs and a name on the dial. Came close once, though. I dropped my dollar pocket watch one day, and before I could find it, the thing had put down roots and grown into a three-dollar alarm clock. But it never kept accurate time.

It was our young'uns who discovered they could tell time by the vegetables. They planted a cucumber seed, and once the vine leaped out of the ground, it traveled along steady as a clock.

"An inch a second," Will said. "Kind of like a second hand."

"Blossoms come out on the minute," Jill said. "Kind of like a minute hand."

They tried other vegetable timepieces. But pole beans had a way of running a mite fast and squash a mite slow.

As I say, those homegrown clocks began running down. I remember my dear wife, Melissa, was boiling three-and-a-half-minute eggs for breakfast. Little Clarinda planted a cucumber seed, and before it grew three blossoms and thirty inches, those eggs were hard-boiled.

"Mercy!" I declared. "Topsoil must be drying out."

Well, the days turned drier and drier. No doubt about it. Our wonderful topsoil was losing some of its get-up-and-go. Why, it took almost a whole day to raise a crop of corn. The young'uns had planted a plum tree, but all it would grow was prunes. Dogs would fight over a dry bone for the moisture in it.

"Willjillhesterchesterpeterpollytimtommarylarryand-littleclarinda!" I called. "Keep your eyes peeled for rain."

They took turns in the tree house scanning the skies, and one night Chester said, "Pa, what if it doesn't rain by Fourth of July? How'll we shoot off firecrackers?"

"Be patient, my lambs," I said. We used to grow our own firecrackers, too. "Why, it's a long spell to Fourth of July."

My, wasn't the next morning a scorcher! The sun came out so hot that our hens laid fried eggs. But no, that wasn't the Big Dry. The young'uns planted watermelons to cool off and beets to keep the mosquitoes away.

"Look!" Polly exclaimed, pointing to the watermelons. "Pa, they're rising off the ground!"

Rising? They began to float in the air like balloons! We could hardly believe our eyes. And gracious me! When we cut those melons open, it turned out they were full of hot air.

Well, I was getting a mite worried myself. Our beets were growing smaller and smaller, and the skeeters were

223

growing larger and larger. Many a time before dawn, a rapping at the windows would wake us out of a sound sleep. It was those confounded, needle-nosed gallinippers pecking away, demanding breakfast.

Then it came—the Big Dry.

Mercy! Our cow began giving powdered milk. We pumped away on our water pump, but all it brought up was dry steam. The oldest boys went fishing and caught six dried catfish.

"Not a rain cloud in sight, Pa," Mary called from the tree house.

"Watch out for gallinippers!" Larry shouted, as a mosquito made a dive at him. The earth was so parched we couldn't raise a crop of beets. And the varmints were getting downright ornery. Then, as I stood there, I felt my shoes getting tighter and tighter.

"Thunderation!" I exclaimed. "Our topsoil's so dry it's gone in reverse. It's shrinking things."

Didn't I lay awake most of the night! Our wonderful one-acre farm might shrink to a square foot. And all night long the skeeters rattled the windows and hammered at the door. Big? The smallest ones must have weighed three pounds. In the moonlight I saw them chase a yellow-billed cuckoo.

Didn't that make me sit up in a hurry! An idea struck me. Glory be! I'd break that drought.

First thing in the morning I took Will and Chester to town with me and rented three wagons and a birdcage. We drove straight home, and I called everyone together.

"Get shovels, my lambs! Heap these wagons full of topsoil!"

But Larry and little Clarinda were still worried about Fourth of July. "We won't be able to grow fireworks, Pa!"

"You have my word," I declared firmly.

Before long, we were on our way. I drove the first wagon, with the young'uns following along behind in the other two. It might be a longish trip, and we had loaded up with picnic hampers of food. We also brought along rolls of chicken wire and our raincoats.

"Where are we going, Pa?" Jill called from the wagon behind.

"Hunting."

"Hunting?" Tom said.

"Exactly, my lambs. We're going to track down a rain cloud and wet down this topsoil."

"But how, Pa?" asked Tim.

I lifted the birdcage from under the wagon seat. "Presto," I said and whipped off the cover. "Look at that lost-looking, scared-looking, long-tailed creature. Found it hiding from the skeeters under a milk pail this morning. It's a genuine rain crow, my lambs."

"A rain crow?" Mary said. "It doesn't look like a crow at all."

"Correct and exactly," I said, smiling. "It looks like a

225

yellow-billed cuckoo, and that's what it is. But don't folks call 'em rain crows? Why, that bird can smell a downpour coming sixty miles away. It rattles its throat and begins to squawk. All we got to do is follow that squawk.''

But you never heard such a quiet bird! We traveled miles and miles across the prairie, this way and the other, and not a rattle out of that rain crow.

The Big Dry had done its mischief everywhere. We didn't see a dog without his tongue dragging. And it took two of them to bark at us once. A farmer told us he hadn't been able to grow anything all year but baked potatoes!

Of course, we slept under chicken wire and covered the horses, too. My, what a racket the gallinippers made!

Day after day we hauled our three loads of topsoil across the prairie, but that rain crow didn't so much as clear its throat.

The young'uns were getting impatient. "Speak up, rain crow," Chester muttered desperately.

"Rattle," Hester pleaded.

"Squawk," said Peter.

"Please," said Mary. "Just a little peep would help."

Not a cloud appeared in the sky. I'll confess I was getting a mite discouraged. And the Fourth of July was less than two weeks off!

We curled up under chicken wire that night, as usual, and the big skeeters kept banging into it, so you could hardly sleep. They rattled like a hailstorm. And suddenly, at daybreak, I rose up laughing.

"Hear that?"

The young'uns crowded around the rain crow. We hadn't been able to hear its voice rattle because of the mosquitoes. Now it turned in its cage, gazed off to the northwest, opened its yellow beak, and let out a real, ear-busting rain cry.

"K-*kawk*! K-*kawk*! K-*kawk*!"

"Put on your raincoats, my lambs!" I said, and we rushed to the wagons.

"K-*kawk*! K-*kawk*! K-*kawk*!"

Didn't we raise dust! That bird faced northwest like a dog on point. There was a rain cloud out there, and before long, Jill gave a shout.

"I see it!"

And the others chimed in one after the other. "Me, too!"

"K-*kawk*! K-*kawk*! K-*kawk*!"

We headed directly for that lone cloud, the young'uns yelling, the horses snorting, and the bird squawking.

Glory be! The first raindrops spattered as large as quarters. And my, didn't the young'uns frolic in that cloudburst! They lifted their faces and opened their mouths and drank right out of the sky. They splashed about and felt mud between their toes for the first time in ages. We all forgot to put on our raincoats and got wet as fish.

Our dried-up topsoil soaked up raindrops like a sponge. It was a joy to behold! But if we stayed longer, we'd get stuck in the mud.

"Back in the wagons!" I shouted. "Home, my lambs, and not a moment to lose."

Well, home was right where we left it.

I got a pinch of onion seeds and went from wagon to wagon, sowing a few seeds in each load of moist earth. I didn't want to crowd those onions.

227

Now, that rich topsoil of ours had been idle a long time; it was rarin' to go. Before I could run back to the house, the greens were up. By the time I could get down my shotgun, the tops had grown four or five feet tall—onions are terrible slow growers. Before I could load my shotgun, the bulbs were finally busting up through the soil.

We stood at the windows watching. Those onion roots were having a great feast. The wagons heaved and creaked as the onions swelled and lifted themselves. They were already the size of pumpkins. But that wasn't near big enough. Soon they were larger'n washtubs and began to shoulder the smaller ones off the wagons.

Suddenly we heard a distant roaring in the air. Those zing-zanging, hot-tempered, blood-sucking prairie mosquitoes were returning from town with their stingers freshly sharpened. The Big Dry hadn't done their dispositions any good; their tempers were at a boil.

"You going to shoot them down, Pa?" Will asked.

"Too many for that," I answered.

"How big do those onions have to grow?" Chester asked.

"How big are they now?"

"A little smaller'n a cow shed."

"That's big enough," I nodded, lifting the window just enough to poke the shotgun through.

Well, the gallinippers spied the onions—I had planted red onions, you know—and came swarming over our farm. I let go at the bulbs with a double charge of buckshot and slammed the window.

"Handkerchiefs, everyone!" I called out. The odor of fresh-cut onion shot through the air, under the door, and through the cracks. Cry? In no time our handkerchiefs were wet as dishrags.

Well! You never saw such surprised gallinippers. They zing-zanged every which way, most of them backwards. And weep? Their eyes began to flow like sprinkling cans. Onion tears! The roof began to leak. Mud puddles formed everywhere. Before long, the downpour was equal to any cloudburst I ever saw. Nearly flooded our farm!

The skeeters kept their distance after that. But they'd been mighty helpful.

With our farm freshly watered we grew tons of great onions—three or four crops a day. We gave them away to farmers all over the county.

The newspaper ran a picture of the whole family and the rain crow, too.

The young'uns had a splendid Fourth of July. They grew all the fireworks they wanted. They'd dash about with bean shooters, shooting radish seeds. You know how fast radishes come up. In our rich topsoil they grew quicker'n the eye. The seeds hardly touched the ground before they took root and swelled up and exploded. They'd go off like strings of firecrackers.

And, mercy, what a racket! Didn't I say I'd rather catch a skunk by the tail than tell a fib? Well, at nightfall a scared cat ran up a tree, and I went up a ladder to get it down. I reached in the branches and caught it by the tail. I'd be lying if I didn't admit the truth. It was a skunk.

Don't Ever Cross a Crocodile

Don't ever cross a crocodile,
However few his faults.
Don't ever dare
A dancing bear
To teach you how to waltz.

Don't ever poke a rattlesnake
Who's sleeping in the sun
And say the poke
Was just a joke
And really all in fun.

Don't ever lure a lion close
With gifts of steak and suet.
Though lion-looks
Are nice in books,
Don't ever, ever do it.

　　　　　　　　　–Kaye Starbird

231

The Story of Deborah

After they had defeated most of the Canaanite kings, the Israelites moved into the land of Canaan. But life there was neither peaceful nor quiet. The original inhabitants of the land were not going to give it up without a fight. The Israelites were tired of war. They hoped to lead a peaceful life. But this seemed impossible unless they forgot the laws of Moses and lived like the people of Canaan.

The people of Canaan still worshiped idols. They were cruel and dirty. They had no law. The Israelites found it easy to forget the laws of Moses and be like the people of Canaan. They said, "If we live like the people around us, they will leave us alone. Let us worship their gods and live in peace."

So the foolish among them began to bow down to idols called Baal and Ashtoreth. But when the other nations saw the Israelites living like themselves, they lost all respect for them. Conditions became worse instead of better.

All the nations began to make war upon the Israelites. At first small bands of robbers would steal their cattle and burn their crops. Then hundreds of men on horseback would raid their cities and villages. In spite of all this, the Israelites managed to drive them away and hold the land.

This went on for a number of years and the Israelites became weaker and weaker. The king of Canaan took advantage of this weakness and began to attack them with a vast army of trained men. Nine hundred of his men rode in iron chariots. The captain of these men was called Sisera.

The Israelites had no leader. There was no one to give them strength and courage, as their great leaders had done in the past. But through all their misery there had been a woman called Deborah to whom the people went for help.

Deborah was a poor woman who lived in the hill country of Ephraim. She firmly believed in the one God and tried to keep the people from worshiping Baal. She had a voice that was soft and low, and people found comfort in her words. She had always said, "Be proud of your people and cherish your faith in one God. Be yourselves, instead of copying the ways of your neighbors."

When the news of the war with the king of Canaan reached the hill country, all the people rushed to Deborah, crying, "What shall we do? What shall we do?"

Deborah answered, "Leave me alone and I will think of a plan. In the meantime send for a young man by the name of Barak, of the tribe of Naphtali."

So the people left Deborah alone and sent messengers to bring Barak. Barak was young and strong. His tribe alone lived in peace, for under his leadership the Canaanites had been driven away.

When Barak stood before Deborah, she said, "I have heard of your courage, Barak. Tell me, have you enough courage to lead an army of ten thousand against Sisera who commands the army of Canaan?"

Barak laughed. "Ten thousand! If I had an army of ten thousand, I would not only wipe out Sisera but all the Canaanites who attack us."

"Then listen to my plan," answered Deborah. "Israel is sleeping. But its warriors will awaken when you call them to war. Send messengers among the people. Tell all the warriors to gather here. In a few days you will have an army of more than ten thousand.

"When I have raised the army, what are your plans?" asked Barak.

233

"You will lead your army to the top of Mount Tabor," answered Deborah.

"Why to the top of the mountain? Wouldn't it be better to hide in the valley below?"

"No," said Deborah. "Sisera has iron chariots which are only useful on level ground. He will be forced to stay in the valley, and you can swoop down upon him from the mountaintop."

"You are wise, Deborah," Barak replied. "Yet I will not go unless you go with me."

Deborah was surprised at Barak's answer. "You mean you have not the courage to go alone?" she cried in anger.

"In order to raise an army, we must rouse these people. You say we have brave warriors," cried Barak, "but they have forgotten everything—their courage, their country, even their God. Come with me, Deborah, and show these people that a woman has courage to lead an army into battle."

Deborah understood. She said, "I will go, Barak. I see you are thinking of your people."

So messengers went from tribe to tribe, asking for people to join Barak and Deborah. In a short time Barak found himself in command of an army of more than ten thousand, all proud and eager to defend their country. Barak and Deborah led the army to the top of Mount Tabor.

In the meantime Sisera had heard of their plans and had completely surrounded the mountain. But Barak had hidden his people all over the top of the mountain. When Sisera attempted to attack, Barak and his army swooped down upon him with such force that Sisera was defeated.

So the army of the king of Canaan was destroyed. There was great rejoicing in Israel. The land was peaceful for forty years.

Lu Pan

DEMI HITZ

Once upon a time there was a boy named Lu Pan who lived with his carpenter father in a village called Lu Family's Bay. When his father was working, Lu Pan liked to help him and see how he used his saws, chisels, and planes to make pieces of furniture.

By the time Lu Pan was ten, he was able to handle all the different carpenter's tools. When his father made stools and cupboards, Lu Pan made little ones.

Once when the boy saw his mother sitting on a floor mat doing her sewing, he made a small chair for her. "Mother," he said, "maybe you can sit on this chair and then your back will not ache."

Lu Pan had a quick mind and nimble fingers. All the neighbors said that he was a promising youngster. Some of them urged his father to take him on as his apprentice. "My hands are too clumsy," his father answered them. "He won't be able to learn much from me. I will send him to a real master carpenter."

When Lu Pan was twelve, his father bought him a fine horse and gave him one hundred taels of silver. "My boy," he said to his son, "take this horse and go to the Chungnang Mountains to find the Master of Carpentry. You will learn from him."

Lu Pan set out for the Chungnang Mountains with a bundle tied across his shoulders. He traveled for many days, climbing big mountains and crossing broad rivers. Would he never find the Master Carpenter and come to the end of his journey?

He stopped for breath at the top of a mountain and was about to give up. Looking around, he saw the roof of a thatched hut. He rode down to the hut, his heart beating fast. When he pushed open the door he saw scattered on the floor all kinds of carpenter's tools—axes, saws, chisels, and hammers. Looking further, he caught sight of a white-bearded old man lying on a bed, fast asleep. Lu Pan was overjoyed. "This must be the Master Carpenter," he thought. Then he tidied up all the tools and sat down to wait for the old man to wake up. Not until the sun was setting did the old man begin to stir.

Lu Pan quickly walked across the room and knelt on the floor in front of the old man. Bowing his head very low, he said: "My name is Lu Pan. I have come all the way from my family's home in distant Lu Family's Bay. Please take me on as your apprentice and teach me your art."

"Why do you wish to learn carpentry?" asked the old man.

"I want to build houses for people, and bridges. I want to work and make things for people," replied the boy.

"Your intentions are good enough. Perhaps I will take you on as my apprentice. First, however, your courage must be tested, as well as your skill. You must mend all these tools." He pointed to the tools lying on the floor.

Lu Pan took the tools to a giant grindstone to sharpen them. He worked hard for seven days and seven nights and put into perfect working order the chisels, axes, saws, and hammers. Then he took them all to the Master, hoping that he would be pleased with the work. The old man merely grunted and said to him, "Now you may fell the big tree that stands in front of my hut."

It was such a huge tree that two men could not link their arms and circle it. Lu Pan hacked and sawed until the tree fell to the ground. Now would the Master be pleased?

237

But no. The Master gave him yet another task. This time he was to make the tree into a smooth, round beam. Wearily Lu Pan took up the axe and struggled with his new task. At last he was finished. He felt he could not do another stroke of work.

This time the old Master was pleased with Lu Pan's work. "Well done, my boy," he said. "I see that no problem is too difficult for you to attempt. You have courage. Now I am ready to teach you all that I know."

He led Lu Pan to a room piled high with models, all of them fine examples of the carpenter's craft. Lu Pan was amazed. "Now take each one of these models apart and put it together again," the Master ordered.

Fascinated by the models, Lu Pan went to work with a will, going into the room every day before dawn. He did not leave it until the stars were bright in the sky. He took apart each one of the models and put them all together again until he knew all the parts by heart. He worked in this fashion in the Master's hut for three whole years.

At the end of the third year, the Master wished to find out just how much Lu Pan had learned. So he burned all the models and ordered the boy to make them himself.

Lu Pan succeeded in remaking all the models from memory. By this time he was fifteen years old and was able to make any new design that the Master ordered.

The Master was content with the progress his apprentice had made. "You have mastered our craft," he told him. "Now it is time for you to leave me."

"Please allow me to remain here for three more years," the boy begged.

"From now on," the Master Carpenter answered, "you will be learning through actual work, out on your own.

And never forget, my young friend, that learning is the work of a lifetime.''

Lu Pan took his leave of the Master. There were tears in his eyes.

As the years passed, Lu Pan became not only a very famous carpenter, but an architect, engineer, inventor, and writer as well.

He built small houses and large houses, winter houses and summer houses, and great halls. He built bridges, and he invented the compass and the lock. He designed the rotary mill. And he made the first kite.

He also wrote *Lu Pan Ching*, or *Lu Pan's Manual*. This book contained many illustrations showing how to cut wood and carve beams, and it told which days were the lucky ones for building.

Lu Pan's methods of carpentry have been followed down through the centuries, and his manual exists today. It is because of the tradition begun by this master that carpentry in China today has maintained a very high level of skill.

Lu Pan, or Kungshu Pan, is considered the greatest of all Chinese artisans. So many legends have grown up around Lu Pan that some people wonder if he ever really existed. He was a real person who lived during the Chou Dynasty in the Fifth Century, B.C. He lived in the State of Lu (Shantung), hence his name, Lu Pan.

239

The Ant and the Grain of Wheat

LEONARDO DA VINCI

A grain of wheat, left alone in the field after the harvest, was waiting for the rain so that it could hide once more beneath the soil.

An ant saw the grain, loaded it onto his back, and plodded painfully away toward his distant hill.

As the ant walked and walked, the grain of wheat seemed to grow heavier and heavier on his weary shoulders.

"Why don't you leave me here?" said the grain of wheat.

The ant replied, "If I leave you behind, we may not have enough provisions for this winter. We ants are so many, and we each have to bring home whatever food we can find."

"But I am not made only to be eaten," went on the grain of wheat. "I am a seed, full of life, and I am supposed to give birth to a plant. Listen, dear ant, let us make an agreement."

The ant, glad to rest a little, put down the grain of wheat and asked, "What agreement?"

"If you leave me here in my field," said the grain of wheat, "and do not take me to your nest, I shall give back to you, after a year, a hundred grains just like me."

The ant stared at the grain disbelievingly.

"Yes, dear ant. Believe what I am telling you. If you give me up today, I shall give you a hundred of me—a hundred grains of wheat for your nest."

The ant thought, "A hundred grains in exchange for one. But that is a miracle. How will you do that?" he asked the grain of wheat.

"That is a mystery," replied the grain of wheat. "It is the mystery of life. Dig a little hole, bury me in it, and return after a year."

The following year the ant returned. The grain of wheat had grown a new plant laden with seeds and so kept its promise.

The Absent Present

NORMAN HUNTER

"Horrible," said the Duke of Dulstodgy. "Absolutely frightful, simply ghastly, and not at all bearable."

He was looking at a huge, ornate inkstand the Queen had given him for Christmas. But he wasn't at all delighted—first because it was a fearsome-looking inkstand and took up so much room on the writing table that there was no room to write, second because he already had no end of inkstands, and third because he never used inkstands. He always wrote with a fountain pen his favorite aunt had given him.

"I know what I'll do," said the Duke. "I'll send it to Connie. I never can think what to give her for her birthday."

242

"Yes," said the Duchess. "And it will serve her right for giving us that terrible vase we can't stand the sight of and that nobody seems able to break accidentally."

So the imperial inkstand was wrapped up in acres of tissue paper with an elegant card saying Best Wishes for Your Birthday and sent off to Connie, Countess of Catchmee-Iffkan. Then the Duke sat down with his favorite fountain pen and wrote to the Queen to thank her for the "handsome and delightful inkstand."

"Help!" cried the Duchess in her best screaming voice. "Help! This is awful. Oh, my goodness, whatever can we do now?"

It was several days later. A message had just arrived saying that Their Majesties the King and Queen would be graciously pleased to come to tea that very day.

"The inkstand!" cried the Duke, clapping his hand to his head and missing it.

"The Queen will be furious if she doesn't see it when she comes," gasped the Duchess.

"We must get it back at once, immediately, this very second," roared the Duke, starting to run around in circles of various sizes. Then he stopped and sent word to Catchmee-Iffkan Castle, asking if the Countess would be kind enough to return the inkstand, which had been sent to her by mistake.

"Regret I cannot return inkstand," came a message back from the Countess, who always talked like a telegram because she had a nephew in the post office. "Sent it to Baron Bunzanbuttah."

"Well, I do think that's a bit ungrateful of her," said the Duchess. "Giving our present away to someone else like that."

"But, my dear," said the Duke, "we gave the Queen's present to her. So we can't say anything."

The Duchess could say a great deal, but the Duke hadn't time to listen. "I must get the inkstand back at all costs," he cried. "Fetch my carriage."

"To Bunzanbuttah Hall and drive like the devil," he shouted, leaping into the carriage.

The driver, who wasn't quite clear how the devil might drive, started with such a jerk that the Duke was shot out of the back of the carriage. He had to run like anything to catch up, which he didn't do till they'd reached the Baron's.

"Puff—puff-puff-gasp!" panted the Duke, rushing into Bunzanbuttah Hall like a secondhand whirlwind. "Inkstand given by—puff—puff—Countess by—puff—gasp—pant—mistake. Must have it—puff—back again." He talked like an out-of-breath telegram himself, although he had no relations in the post office.

But alas, alack, oh, dearie dearie, tut tut, and goodness gracious! The Baron had already presented the precious inkstand to the Marquis of Mumswerd.

So off the Duke had to dash again. And he arrived at Mumswerd Mansion panting twice as fast as before. But he learned that the hard-to-find inkstand had been passed on by the Marquis to Lady Lilly Letsgo, because he thought she was a bit special.

It was twice as far as goodness knows how far to Letsgo Lodge, but at last the Duke got there, almost in bits. He flung himself through the front door, collapsed into Lady Lilly's drawing room, and gasped out what he wanted.

"Well, really," said Lady Lilly. "Disgraceful I call it, you know." She was almost invisible among seventy-five luxurious cushions, three pet doggies, and eight kittens. "I gave that inkstand to the Queen not so long ago. How the Marquis got hold of it I don't pretend to know."

"Whereizzit?" panted the Duke, clawing at the carpet.

"If you really want the thing," went on Lady Lilly, "you'd better take it, I'm sure. Nobody else seems to appreciate it."

She slid gracefully out of the cushions, scattering kittens and pet doggies all over the place, and slithered into the next room. She immediately let out assorted screams.

The inkstand wasn't on the writing table between the brass candlesticks her Aunt Hetty had given her.

Terrible! Their Majesties would arrive at the Duke's at any moment now, and no inkstand.

"Who did you give it to?" panted the Duke. "Tell me, quick, tell me. I must get it back. Oh, oh, oh."

Just then Lord Letsgo, Lady Lilly's grandpa, came in. He looked at the Duke through a little eyeglass on a stick.

"Who is this person, my dear?" he said to Lady Lilly.

"I am the Duke of Dulstodgy," cried the Duke. "And kindly do not look at me through that little spyglass. I have come for the inkstand that by a series of unfortunate errors was given to Lady Lilly and is now missing."

"Oh, the inkstand!" said Lord Letsgo in a very high-class voice. "Knowing that you never used it, my dear, I sent it to the Queen as a little token of . . ."

"You sent it to the Queen!" screeched Lady Lilly and the Duke, both at once but in different voices.

"This is awful," cried the Duke. "Quick, quick to the palace!"

All three of them shot out of the house, but they were too late. They met the messenger coming out of the palace after delivering the inkstand. All was lost. They were undone.

But no. It wasn't and they weren't. The Duke was a bit undone because some of his vest buttons had burst off in all his travels. But there was still a chance. Their Majesties had already left the palace. The package hadn't been opened.

Frantically the Duke snatched it from the royal footmen, tore off the wrapping to make sure it was the inkstand, and went rushing back to his house with the wind whistling past his ears.

He wasn't a minute too soon. The royal coach was just pulling up to the front door of his house. The Duke dashed around to the back and climbed in through a window. There he had a slight struggle with his own butler, who thought he was a burglar and tried to hit him with a poker. Fortunately the butler missed him and hit the inkstand instead, which was so sturdy that it broke the poker.

"At last!" gasped the Duke, quickly setting the inkstand on the writing table and dashing out to help the Duchess greet the King and Queen.

But the King and Queen hadn't come. Out of the royal coach stepped the Lord High Equerry, who bowed so low to the Duke and Duchess that his hat fell off.

"Their Majesties send their most regretful apologies," he said. "They have been called away on a private visit to their daughter and are therefore unable to come to tea today."

The Duke looked at the Duchess and felt that he was coming to a boil.

"Oh, what a shame," said the Duchess. "But," she went on, "tea is all ready, and it seems a pity to waste it. So perhaps Your Excellency would care to . . ."

The Lord High Equerry didn't wait for her to finish. He went straight in and began to eat the cream rolls. The Duke and Duchess joined him happily. The situation was saved. The inkstand was back. They'd have it chained to the writing table in case the Queen ever did call.

But the Duke can never bring himself to look at it. He gets all out of breath, remembering the frantic and unnecessary chase.

The Army of Two

PATRICIA EDWARDS CLYNE

Becky Bates shielded her blue eyes as she gazed across the harbor. In the distance the town of Scituate, Massachusetts, lay sparkling in the September sun.

"I still don't understand why we couldn't go along too!" Becky declared.

"Someone had to stay behind to help Mother," her sister Abigail pointed out.

"But Mother said she didn't need any help!" Becky stamped her foot, though it made no sound in the coarse sand of Cedar Point.

"Well, what if Father doesn't return from town before sunset? Someone must be here to start the beacon in the lighthouse," Abigail reminded her. "Then there's always the chance that the British . . ."

Both girls stared again at the quiet waters of Scituate Harbor. There was no wreckage there now, but they would never forget what it had looked like on June 11, 1814. That was the terrible day three months ago when the British had raided Scituate. By the time the Redcoats sailed away, the harbor had been turned into an inferno of burning ships.

"The British wouldn't dare come back," Becky stated boldly. "Not since our soldiers have been stationed here at the lighthouse."

"But the soldiers aren't here today," Abigail was quick to say. "And neither is Father."

An uneasy feeling gripped Becky. Abigail was right. The American troops, restless after months of idleness, had begun to spend their days across the harbor in Scituate. The girls' father was unhappy over the careless attitude of the regiment, but there was little he could do about it. He was only the lighthouse keeper and had no authority over the soldiers.

Becky sighed as she turned back to the lighthouse. "Well, we might

248

as well go see if there isn't some way we can help Mother, after all."

The long, narrow arm of land that was called Cedar Point curved around to protect the harbor of Scituate. Because of this, the girls did not get a glimpse of the blue-gray waters of the Atlantic Ocean until they had almost reached the lighthouse.

"A frigate! It's a British frigate!"

Abigail's cry made Becky's heart lurch, and she strained her eyes to identify the vessel fast approaching the harbor. Suddenly the wind caught the flag at the peak of the mast, unfurling it to full length. It was the fearsome British Union Jack!

Legs churning in the sand, the two girls raced for the lighthouse. "Mother! Mother, it's the British. They're coming again!"

By the time they reached the door, Mrs. Bates had opened it, and the girls hurried inside.

"We must alert the regiment!" Mrs. Bates cried. "We must warn the people!" Quickly untying her

apron, she took her bonnet from a peg near the door, and the three of them hurried outside.

But it was too late. The British frigate had already dropped anchor and launched two barges full of soldiers.

"There is no way to warn the people in Scituate now," Mrs. Bates said gloomily. "The British would see us if we tried to row the dory across the harbor. And it would take too long to go the roundabout way by land. I think it best that we hide ourselves among the cedars and sand dunes."

So saying, she began to walk away from the lighthouse. Then sensing that her two daughters were not following, she turned abruptly, an impatient look on her face.

Abigail was tugging at her sister's sleeve. But Becky only stood there, staring at the oncoming barges. "Hide ourselves," she was murmuring. "So the British won't see us."

Then she shouted, "That's it! The British can't see us among the dunes! Come on, Abigail!"

Abigail could only stare in amazement as Becky darted back into the lighthouse. Then Abigail turned to call, "Go ahead, Mother. I'll fetch Becky."

When Abigail stepped over the threshold, Becky was struggling to lift a heavy drum the American soldiers had left behind. "Help me, Abigail," she pleaded. "But first get the fife over there. Papa taught me how to play 'Yankee Doodle.' Remember?"

Abigail shook her head in bewildered agitation. "Of course I remember," she said. "But what has 'Yankee Doodle' got to do with this? As for the drum, there's no time to save it. Come on, Becky. The British will be landing at any minute. We must get to the dunes!"

"Indeed we must," Becky agreed. "But the drum and the fife must go too!"

Fully convinced that her older sister had lost her senses from fright, Abigail decided to humor her. "All right, Becky. If you insist on having the drum and fife, we'll take them along. Only hurry!"

When the girls arrived behind the sand dune where their mother waited, Becky breathlessly explained what she had in mind. She paused only to hand the drumsticks to Abigail before she put the wooden fife to her lips.

Meanwhile, the British soldiers stirred restlessly in the barges, their eyes intent on the rocky beach that sloped up to the lighthouse. Not a word was said as they nervously clutched their guns.

Suddenly the silence was shattered by the staccato tapping of a drum. The Redcoats jerked to attention, straining to make out the pattern of the drumbeats.

Just as the soldiers turned apprehensive eyes to the officer in charge, the shrill voice of a fife joined the thump of the drum. It took only a few notes for them to recognize the detested American tune "Yankee Doodle."

The British commander aboard the frigate also heard the warning of the fife and drum. He had counted on surprising the Americans, for his landing party was not a large one. But now there would be no surprise. Nor was there any way of telling how many Americans might be waiting for them behind the dunes.

Within seconds, the commander's decision was made. He signaled the barges to return to the frigate.

Behind a sand dune on shore, a dark head popped up, and a pair of blue eyes grew wide with delight.

"Hurrah!" came a triumphant shout.

But the British did not hear it. With the landing party safely back on board, they had hoisted sail and were fast making for the open Atlantic. Nor did they spot the two young girls, joyously dancing around a dark red drum on shore.

Only later did the British commander of the frigate *La Hogue* find out that he had been frightened away by a pair of heroic teen-age sisters, who would forever be proudly remembered as the "Army of Two."

Across a Continent

GILBERT GRAIL

In the same year that Christopher Columbus returned to Spain after finding a new world across the Atlantic, Álvar Núñez Cabeza de Vaca was born in the Spanish town of Jerez. While de Vaca was growing up, the Spanish were extending their conquests in the New World. Ponce de León reached Florida; Balboa discovered the Pacific Ocean; and Cortés found the vast riches of Mexico.

The young de Vaca was more interested in following the family tradition of soldiering than in finding the wealth of America. When he was nineteen, de Vaca fought in the battle of Ravenna in Italy. This day-long battle was the first in which both sides used a new weapon—the cannon. Twenty thousand soldiers were killed on that April day. De Vaca, one of the few survivors, was sickened by the slaughter and resolved to give up the soldier's life.

Some years later the Spanish king appointed de Vaca governor of a small district in southern Spain. He married and settled down to a quiet life. This quiet life came to an end, however, when Panfilo de Narváez came to de Vaca's town in 1526.

Narváez was a tall, loud adventurer who had spent many years in the New World. He was convinced that the unknown land of Florida contained more gold than Cortés had found in Mexico, and he believed that a golden city called Cibola existed somewhere in this unexplored region. He persuaded de Vaca to join the expedition he was organizing to find Cibola. Since de Vaca contributed much of his own money, he was made treasurer and second-in-command of the expedition.

Before the ships sailed from Spain in the summer of 1527, de Vaca visited his friend Father Las Casas, who had spent twenty years in the New World. Distressed by the newcomers' brutal treatment of the native Indians, Las Casas had made up a list of rules to protect these natives and had persuaded the Spanish king to order Narváez to obey these rules.

"If there is any brutality," he told de Vaca, "you must report it. I know that cunning wolf Narváez is going to laugh at the king's orders. So you must do all you can to see that they are carried out."

The five tiny ships of the expedition, overloaded with 600 men as well as a great many horses, cows, and pigs, began the expedition across the Atlantic. It was a nightmare from beginning to end. When the ships finally reached Santo Domingo, 140 men promptly deserted. Sailing on to Cuba, two of the five ships were wrecked in a hurricane.

After Narváez bought supplies in Cuba, he decided to postpone the voyage to Florida until the hurricane season was over. It was at this time that one of the sailors, an African named Esteban, suggested that the three remaining ships be painted with a mixture of tar and chopped horsehair to protect them from the deadly borer worms of the Caribbean. For the first time de Vaca took notice of the wise African who was to play an important role in the expedition. Esteban's suggestion probably kept the ships seaworthy.

While they were waiting in Cuba, several of the men went to a gypsy fortuneteller. Asking what the expedition would bring them, they were answered with one word—"death." Pressing her for more information, they were told that all but four of the men would meet death on the expedition. "And those four are not here," the fortuneteller added, looking closely at all of their faces.

On the first day of March 1528, the three ships and 400 men set sail for Florida. The excitement of approaching a rich and unknown land was hindered by seasickness and growing distrust of Narváez. After six miserable weeks at sea, the ships sailed into what is now Tampa Bay.

Ashore, the expedition found a deserted Indian village. In it one of the men discovered a baby's rattle made of gold. Surely the golden city of Cibola could not be far!

255

The Spaniards saw the first native Americans that afternoon. They came out of the forest carrying long bows and arrows and motioned to the newcomers that they should return to their ships and go. It was clear to the Spaniards that they must move on.

A decision had to be made. Narváez believed that Cibola lay to the north. The question was whether to try to reach it by land or by sea. One of the young officers, Dorantes, declared he had had enough of the sea and favored an overland march. Because of the golden toy, he thought the fabulous city must be near. De Vaca favored going by sea because of the dangers of travel in the forests.

Narváez made the worst of all possible decisions. Anxious to move on, he divided the expedition into two groups. Some of the men would go north in the ships, but most of them, including Narváez and de Vaca, would march through the forests and swamps. The two groups would meet at the next bay.

This meeting did not come about, however. The ships were never seen again. Narváez, de Vaca, and 300 men were now cut off from the rest of the world.

They encountered many hardships as they marched north through heavy forests and wide swamps. The heat was almost unbearable. Swarms of mosquitoes gave the weary marchers no peace. In the first three days nine men and three horses died by drowning or from snakebite.

De Vaca pleaded with his commander to move to the seashore to wait for the ships. Narváez refused. Cibola and all its wealth was near; he was sure of it. The Spaniards pressed on for another hundred miles and reached the Suwanee River in what is now northern Florida. There the Suwanee Indian tribe welcomed the hungry men and gave them food. The Suwanees were repaid by being forced out of their village.

The next night a shower of arrows fell on the village. Four Spaniards were killed by the invisible foe. Narváez decided to move on.

Hearing that Cibola lay to the northwest, Narváez altered their course. Leeches joined the mosquitoes to torment them. Fever added to their woes. Half their horses were dead. They had reached the northwestern corner of what is now the state of Florida, and there they finally found Cibola. But it was not a great city such as Cortés had found in Mexico. It was a collection of mud huts.

Hunger, the summer heat, and gold fever had so affected the exhausted travelers that they attacked the village without delay. There was no resistance since the men of the village were away. Ignoring the king's orders, Narváez enslaved the women and children, making them gather food. The invaders searched for gold, but there was none.

De Vaca and Dorantes talked over the situation. "These are strange slaves," Dorantes said. "They obey us, but they are not afraid of us. There is something we don't know."

What that something was, the Spaniards found out a few days later. The Suwanee men had returned and were watching their village from the forest. Nine Spanish soldiers who ventured outside the village were killed by arrows four feet long.

The terrified Spaniards remained in the village for three weeks. They did not understand this kind of silent warfare. Then, on a dark night, they began a retreat to the coast. They were followed by the Indians with their terrible long arrows. De Vaca himself was wounded, and many were killed.

After three weeks the Spaniards reached the coast of the Gulf of Mexico. They set up a camp and waited for the ships that would take them back to Cuba. All thought of gold was gone, even from the greedy Narváez. The ships, of course, never came.

A nighttime attack on the camp cost the Spaniards twenty more lives. Narváez now had only half of the 400 men who had landed with him at Tampa Bay. Most of them were weak from hunger and fever.

Now de Vaca was able to convince his weary commander that it was time to take to the sea. The nearest Spanish settlement was at Tampico in Mexico. By sailing across the Gulf of Mexico, the battered group might reach it.

They would have to build five barges, each capable of carrying

257

forty men. Luckily, they had a few saws and axes, and there were plenty of oak and walnut trees nearby. The African, Esteban, had the knowledge to plan the length and width of the barges and the fitting of masts. Sails were made by piecing together old shirts and blankets.

De Vaca helped the blacksmith change melted horseshoes into nails. Another officer, Castillo, and some of the men collected pine resin to fill in the spaces between the planks. Dorantes took care of the sick and wounded. Esteban supervised the entire project. Narváez brooded over the failure of his great plans to find gold and power.

Months passed. It was January of 1529 before the five barges were ready to put to sea for Mexico. They would have to follow the coastline, a distance of nearly a thousand miles. The sails were hoisted, and the barges set off on their desperate voyage. None of the men were expert seamen, so it was vital that the barges always keep in sight of one another and of the land. Every few days they had to go ashore for water and fruit.

But food was not easy to find. Once the barges came ashore to bury six men who had died from hunger and exposure. The surviving men, unable to find food, huddled under some trees, hungry and discouraged. A group of Indians happened by and then disappeared. But the Indians soon returned with baskets of beans and corn, turkeys, and fish. The once arrogant Spaniards accepted these gifts with tears of gratitude. Even the once haughty Narváez presented the leader of the Indians with a silver necklace.

Then the five barges once again moved slowly westward. Their troubles were not over, however. The current from the Mississippi River pushed them far out to sea. As they struggled to get back within sight of land, the barges were separated. Three of them drifted out to sea and were never seen again. Narváez was on one of these, his dreams of glory ended forever. A few days later both de Vaca's and Esteban's barges were wrecked on rocks off the coast of what is now Texas. All aboard were drowned except de Vaca, Esteban, Dorantes, and Castillo.

The four survivors soon fell in with friendly Indians and lived with them for three years. In the spring of 1532 they said farewell to their kindly hosts and started westward on foot. De Vaca figured that they were about 500 miles from Tampico.

Within a week the four were captured by a fierce tribe and made slaves by their captors. Two years went by before they were able to escape. They then fell in with another friendly tribe and accompanied them across what is now southwestern Texas.

259

During this trip de Vaca's three companions became very sick. De Vaca gave them some Indian medicines that he had mixed. Their quick recoveries impressed the Indians, who then brought their own sick to de Vaca. De Vaca taught his three companions his new medical secrets, and soon they had established a far-reaching reputation.

It was now the spring of 1535. It had been seven years since they had landed with Narváez at Tampa Bay. It was time to move on.

With their reputation as medicine men preceding them, they journeyed on to the Rio Grande River. Tampico was to the south, but there was a forbidding desert to be crossed. Instead, de Vaca decided that they should follow the Rio Grande until they could turn south and take a more hospitable route.

None presented itself, however, and they followed the Rio Grande until it abruptly turned north. Then they proceeded to the Sierra Madre Mountains. Moving from tribe to tribe, they successfully practiced their primitive medicine and became known as the "children of the sun."

In September of 1536 de Vaca and his companions came to the Gulf of California, a part of the Pacific Ocean. They were the first men in history to cross the North American continent. Their nine-year journey was all recorded in a diary that de Vaca had begun when the expedition first landed on the coast. The world had its first picture of the great unknown region they had traveled across.

Six months later the men came to a Spanish settlement on the west coast of Mexico. The gypsy's prophecy had come true—only four men had survived the Narváez expedition.

Eldorado

Gaily bedight,
   A gallant knight,
In sunshine and in shadow,
   Had journeyed long,
   Singing a song,
In search of Eldorado.

   But he grew old—
   This knight so bold—
And o'er his heart a shadow
   Fell as he found
   No spot of ground
That looked like Eldorado.

   And, as his strength
   Failed him at length,
He met a pilgrim shadow—
   "Shadow," said he,
   "Where can it be—
This land of Eldorado?"

   "Over the Mountains
   Of the Moon,
Down the Valley of the Shadow,
   Ride, boldly ride,"
   The shade replied,—
"If you seek for Eldorado!"

          —Edgar Allan Poe

Make Hay While the Sun Shines

LAURA INGALLS WILDER

In this excerpt from *The Long Winter*, the Ingalls family is living in a tarpaper claim shanty on their homestead near Silver Lake in the Dakota Territory.

The mowing machine's whirring sounded cheerfully from the old buffalo wallow south of the claim shanty, where bluestem grass stood thick and tall and Pa was cutting it for hay.

The sky was high and quivering with heat over the shimmering prairie. Half-way down to sunset, the sun blazed as hotly as at noon. The wind was scorching hot. But Pa had hours of mowing yet to do before he could stop for the night.

Laura drew up a pailful of water from the well at the edge of the Big Slough. She rinsed the brown jug till it was cool to her hand. Then she filled it with the fresh, cool water, corked it tightly, and started with it to the hayfield.

Swarms of little white butterflies hovered over the path. A dragon-fly with gauzy wings swiftly chased a gnat. On the stubble of cut grass the striped gophers were scampering. All at once they ran for their lives and dived into their holes. Then Laura saw a swift shadow and looked up at the eyes and the claws of a hawk overhead. But all the little gophers were safe in their holes.

Pa was glad to see Laura with the water jug. He got down from the mowing machine and drank a mouthful.

"Ah! that hits the spot!" he said, and tipped up the jug again. Then he corked it, and setting it on the ground he covered it with cut grass.

"This sun almost makes a fellow want a bunch of sprouts to make a shade," he joked. He was really glad there were no trees; he had grubbed so many sprouts from his clearing in the Big Woods, every summer. Here on the Dakota prairies there was not a single tree, not one sprout, not a bit of shade anywhere.

"A man works better when he's warmed up, anyway!" Pa said cheerfully, and chirruped to the horses. Sam and David plodded on, drawing the machine. The long, steel-toothed blade went steadily whirring against the tall grass and laid it down flat. Pa rode high on the open iron seat, watching it lie down, his hand on the lever.

Laura sat in the grass to watch him go once around. The heat there smelled as good as an oven when bread is baking. The little brown-and-yellow-striped gophers were hurrying again, all about her. Tiny birds fluttered and flew to cling to bending grass-stems, balancing lightly. A striped garter snake came flowing and curving through the forest of grass. Sitting hunched with her chin on her knees, Laura felt suddenly as big as a mountain when the snake curved up its head and stared at the high wall of her calico skirt.

Its round eyes were shining like beads, and its tongue was flickering so fast that it looked like a tiny jet of steam. The whole bright-striped snake had a gentle look. Laura knew that garter snakes will not harm anyone, and they are good to have on a farm because they eat the insects that spoil crops.

It stretched its neck low again and, making a perfectly square turn in itself because it could not climb over Laura, it went flowing around her and away in the grass.

Then the mowing machine whirred louder and the horses came nodding their heads slowly in time with their feet. David jumped when Laura spoke almost under his nose.

"Whoa!" Pa said, startled. "Laura! I thought you'd gone. Why are you hiding in the grass like a prairie chicken?"

"Pa," Laura said, "why can't *I* help you make hay? Please let me, Pa. Please."

Pa lifted his hat and ran his fingers through his sweat-damp hair, standing it all on end and letting the wind blow through it. "You're not very big nor strong, little Half-Pint."

"I'm going on fourteen," Laura said. "I can help, Pa. I know I can."

The mowing machine had cost so much that Pa had no money left to pay for help. He could not trade work, because there were only a few homesteaders in this new country and they were busy on their own claims. But he needed help to stack the hay.

"Well," Pa said, "maybe you can. We'll try it. If you can, by George! we'll get this haying done all by ourselves!"

Laura could see that the thought was a load off Pa's mind and she hurried to the shanty to tell Ma.

"Why, I guess you can," Ma said doubtfully. She did not like to see women working in the fields. Only foreigners did that. Ma and her girls were Americans, above doing men's work. But Laura's helping in the hay would solve the problem. She decided, "Yes, Laura, you may."

Carrie eagerly offered to help. "I'll carry the drinking water out to you. I'm big enough to carry the jug!" Carrie was almost ten, but small for her age.

"And I'll do your share of the housework, besides mine," Mary offered happily. She was proud that she could wash dishes and make beds as well as Laura, though she was blind.

The sun and hot wind cured the cut grass so quickly that Pa raked it up next day. He raked it into long windrows, then he raked the windrows into big haycocks. And early the next morning, while the dawn was still cool and meadow-larks were singing, Laura rode to the field with Pa in the hayrack.

There Pa walked beside the wagon and drove the horses between the rows of haycocks. At every haycock he stopped the horses and pitched the hay up into the hayrack. It came tumbling loosely over the high edge and Laura trampled it down. Up and down and back and forth she trampled the loose hay with all the might of her legs, while the forkfuls kept coming over and falling, and she went on trampling while the wagon jolted on to the next haycock. Then Pa pitched more hay in from the other side.

Under her feet the hay climbed higher, trampled down as solid as hay can be. Up and down, fast and hard, her legs kept going, the length of the hayrack and back, and across the middle. The sunshine was hotter and the smell of the hay rose up sweet and strong. Under her feet it bounced and over the edges of the hayrack it kept coming.

All the time she was rising higher on the trampled-down hay. Her head rose above the edges of the rack and she could have looked at the prairie, if she could have stopped trampling. Then the rack was full of hay and still more came flying up from Pa's pitchfork.

Laura was very high up now and the slippery hay was sloping downward around her. She went on trampling carefully. Her face and her neck were wet with sweat and sweat trickled down her back. Her sunbonnet hung by its strings and her braids had come undone. Her long brown hair blew loose in the wind.

Then Pa stepped up on the whiffletrees. He rested one foot on David's broad hip and clambered up onto the load of hay.

"You've done a good job, Laura," he said. "You tramped the hay down so well that we've got a big load on the wagon."

Laura rested in the prickly warm hay while Pa drove near to the stable. Then she slid down and sat in the shade of the wagon. Pa pitched down some hay, then climbed down and spread it evenly to make the big, round bottom of a stack. He climbed onto the load and pitched more hay, then climbed down and leveled it on the stack and trampled it down.

"I could spread it, Pa," Laura said, "so you wouldn't have to keep climbing up and down."

Pa pushed back his hat and leaned for a minute on the pitchfork. "Stacking's a job for two, that's a fact," he said. "This way takes too much time. Being willing helps a lot, but you're not very big, little Half-Pint." She could only get him to say, "Well, we'll see." But when they came back with the next load he gave her a pitchfork and let her try. The long fork was taller than she was and she did not know how to use it, so she handled it clumsily. But while Pa tossed the hay from the wagon she spread it as well as she could, walking around and around on the stack to pack it tightly. In spite of the best she could do, Pa had to level the stack for the next load.

Now the sun and the wind were hotter and Laura's legs quivered while she made them trample the hay. She was glad to rest for the little times between the field and the stack. She was thirsty, then she was thirstier, and then she was so thirsty that she could think of nothing else. It seemed forever till ten o'clock when Carrie came lugging the jug half-full.

Pa told Laura to drink first but not too much. Nothing was ever so good as that cool wetness going down her throat. At the taste of it she stopped in surprise and Carrie clapped her hands and cried out, laughing, "Don't tell, Laura, don't tell till Pa tastes it!"

Ma had sent them ginger-water. She had sweetened the cool well-water with sugar, flavored it with vinegar, and put in plenty of ginger to warm their stomachs so they could drink till they were not thirsty. Ginger-water would not make them sick, as plain cold water would when they were so hot. Such a treat made that ordinary day into a special day, the first day that Laura helped in the haying.

Cluster 6

Four-Legs

TOM McGOWEN

Tall-tree had killed a fine, fat bird and was on his way
back to the tribal caves when he came across the wolf
cub. It was lying with the back of its body pinned among
the branches of a fallen tree. There had been a storm
during the night, and a howl of wind had torn the dead
trunk in two and sent it crashing to the ground. The
frightened cub, although unhurt, had been trapped
among the branches when the tree fell.

It was a very young cub and quite small, but meat was
meat, and Tall-tree lifted his spear. Then he paused. It
had come to him that babies have a way of growing
bigger. If he kept the cub until it grew to full size, it
would provide a great deal more meat.

The thought seemed to be a good one, so Tall-tree
unwrapped a strip of leather that he had twined around
his forearm. He tied the cub's front legs together. It
growled and snapped at him, but its teeth were too small
to damage his tough skin. When the animal's front legs
were secured, Tall-tree heaved aside the branches and
yanked the cub free. It scratched furiously at him with its
back legs until he tied them too. Then Tall-tree went on
his way.

Coming to the place of caves, he went to the great fire
to turn over what he had caught as he was supposed to.
Old Bent-leg sat before the fire, his good leg tucked
beneath him and the withered one, crushed by a bison

many snows ago, was stretched out. Bent-leg kept tally on the game that young hunters brought. Tall-tree dropped the bird on the small pile of animals near the old man's leg. Bent-leg nodded and then jerked his head toward the wolf cub that hung, whining, from Tall-tree's hand.

"What is that?" grunted the old hunter.

"A small four-legs night-howler," replied Tall-tree, giving his people's name for the animal. "It came to me that I could keep it tied in my cave and feed it scraps from my own food. When it is full grown, we can kill it for its meat."

271

Bent-leg frowned but then realized the cleverness of Tall-tree's thinking. "That is good!" he exclaimed. "It is little meat now, but it will be much meat later!"

Food was always a problem for the tribe. Every day the men hunted for animals and birds while the women and children searched for roots, berries, and insects that could be eaten. Everything that was found was shared by the tribe, and often there was hardly enough.

Tall-tree walked to his cave. Near the entrance was a large boulder, beside which he dropped the squirming cub. From the cave he brought several thin strips of animal hide. These he knotted together to make a rope, which he quickly tied around the cub's neck, avoiding its snapping teeth. Then, with a grunt, he tipped the boulder up and kicked the free end of the rope beneath it. Letting the boulder settle back with a thump, he untied the animal's legs.

The cub rolled to its feet, shook itself, and made a dash for freedom, only to have its legs jerked out from under it as the rope pulled it to an abrupt stop. Seeing that the four-legs was firmly tethered, Tall-tree nodded and entered his cave.

The midafternoon sun was high and hot when he came out later. Tall-tree glanced at the four-legs. Its head was down, its tail drooped, and it panted noisily. The thought came to Tall-tree that if he were the four-legs, tied in the hot sun all this time, he would be thirsty. Unslinging the animal-skin water bag that hung over his shoulder, he untied its mouth and poured a small puddle onto the ground. The cub growled faintly but inched forward and began to lap the water.

Tall-tree frowned. He would often be gone for long

trips, and he wondered how to keep the cub supplied with water during his absence. He didn't want it to die of thirst.

He went into the cave for his sharp-edged digging stone. Outside again, he began chopping at the sandy soil. Growling, the four-legs backed away as far as the leather rope would let it and glared at him.

In a short time Tall-tree had made a hole that seemed suitably deep. He lined the hole with an animal skin, weighting down the edges with small rocks. Then he emptied his water bag into the hole. The skin held the water. The four-legs now had its own water hole, which would keep it from getting thirsty. Tall-tree grunted in approval and left.

When he returned later, he carried several meaty bones left from his share of food at the tribal fire. He dropped these before the four-legs. Although it growled at him, he could hear its teeth scraping on the bones from within his cave.

Every day thereafter Tall-tree put fresh water into the four-legs's hole, brought it scraps of meat, and cleaned up after it. After many days had passed, he noticed a change. The four-legs no longer growled at him when he came near. In fact, when it saw him coming now, it would stand and watch him, moving its tail back and forth in an odd way. Tall-tree realized it no longer feared him. He found it pleasant to have the little animal acting friendly toward him. He was surprised to find himself talking to it as though it were a child.

"Here is your meat, Four-legs," he would call as he approached with a handful of scraps. "Are you thirsty, Four-legs?" he would ask as he filled its water hole. The animal's ears would twitch and its tail would move back and forth at the sound of his voice.

And Tall-tree no longer had to guard against the cub's teeth. Instead of tossing the meat and bones to the animal, he now let the cub take them from his hand. And once, as he was filling the water hole, the four-legs pushed its nose against his hand and licked it. Tall-tree jerked his hand back in surprise. But then, hesitantly, he held it out again. Once more the pink tongue flashed out, and the bushy tail fanned the air furiously. Tall-tree grinned.

After that he began to play a game with the wolf cub. Whenever he approached the cave, he would try to surprise the animal by coming from a different direction or by moving stealthily. But always the four-legs would be staring straight at him, straining at the rope and beating the air with its tail.

Then one day Tall-tree was bringing the catch from his hunting to the fire when Bent-leg peered up at him. "Is the four-legs fat enough?" asked Bent-leg.

Tall-tree hesitated. He had nearly forgotten his reason for keeping the cub. "Not yet," he said uncomfortably.

"Soon, eh?" asked Bent-leg. Tall-tree nodded and hurried away.

At his cave he squatted and looked anxiously at the wolf cub. It had grown, and before long it would be as big as it was going to get. Then he would have to turn it over to be meat for the tribe, as he had promised.

But he didn't want the four-legs to die. Something had happened to him and to it. Perhaps because it had been so little when he found it, it had not grown up to be like other wolves that showed their teeth at people and

ran from them. Instead of being a wild wolf, Four-legs
was more like a child that liked him. And he liked it!

The next day Tall-tree went hunting determined to
bring back more game than ever before. Perhaps, he
thought, if he brought plenty of meat, Bent-leg would
forget about the wolf. But the hunt went badly. He
returned with only a young squirrel. To his dismay, none
of the other hunters had fared well either. The pile of
birds and animals by the fire was smaller than usual.

"It is not enough!" said Bent-leg. "We must have the
four-legs now, Tall-tree."

"Wait a few days," said Tall-tree. "The hunting may
grow even harder. We may need the four-legs even more
then."

Bent-leg did not press him, so he hurried away. At his
cave he knelt beside the wolf and rubbed its head. It
nudged him with a cold nose and swept the ground with
its tail.

That night, lying beside the fire in his cave, he knew
that the next day or the day after that he would have to

275

give the wolf to the tribe. Dreading the dawn, he fell asleep.

It seemed like only seconds later that something suddenly awakened him. It was Four-legs, snarling furiously.

Tall-tree was on his feet in an instant. Snatching his spear, he peered over the nearly dead fire. In the moonlight Four-legs stood before the cave, snarling and showing its teeth, its fur bristling. Beyond it green eyes gleamed and scales glinted on a long, winding body. There was an evil hiss and a rattling sound. The hair at the back of Tall-tree's neck rose as he saw the great snake, poised to sink its poisonous fangs into the wolf's body.

Tall-tree exploded into action. Leaping over the fire, he swung his spear forward like a club, slamming it into the snake's body just below the swaying head. The heavy blow knocked the serpent to the ground. Springing after it, Tall-tree smashed the spear again and again into the snake's head.

After a time Tall-tree leaned on his spear, panting heavily. Although the snake's body still feebly twisted, he knew it was dead. Four-legs knew it was dead too, and stopped growling.

Tall-tree knew what had happened. Drawn by the heat of the fire, the snake had crawled toward the cave. It would have been attracted by the warmth of Tall-tree's body and probably would have coiled itself next to him. If he had disturbed it, the creature would have bitten him. He remembered when just such a snake had bitten a man. The man had raved with pain and then died. Tall-tree shivered. If Four-legs had not growled and wakened him, he also might have died.

Tall-tree fed the fire until it blazed up again. Then he dragged the snake into the cave and began to skin it. When he finished, he gazed thoughtfully at the thick coils of white meat.

At dawn he hurried to the tribal fire, carrying the snake meat. Bent-leg was already there, as were several hunters, waiting for a lighter sky before starting on their way. Among them was Green-leaf, the tribe's leader. Tall-tree dumped the coils of meat near Bent-leg's feet.

"I have meat for the tribe," he said, looking at Green-leaf. "I will hunt for other meat today, but I bring this meat now."

The men stared at the white coils. "Where did you find this long-crawler?" asked Green-leaf.

"It came to my cave, seeking warmth as long-crawlers do after sundown," Tall-tree replied. "I killed it."

"Were you bitten?" asked Green-leaf, looking at him anxiously.

Tall-tree shook his head. "I might have been bitten," he said. "But the four-legs tied at my cave woke me with its growling. It saved my life." He looked into Green-leaf's eyes. "I was going to give the four-legs as meat for the tribe. Let me give this meat instead, Green-leaf. Let the four-legs live!"

Green-leaf considered his words. "I do not know what an animal is good for, except to eat. What will you do with the four-legs?"

"I will set it free," answered Tall-tree.

The chieftain thought. "It is well," he said at last. "You promised the tribe meat, and you brought more meat than you promised. The four-legs saved you to hunt for the tribe. Let it go then, if that is your wish."

Tall-tree walked slowly back to his cave. He was glad
that the wolf would not have to die. Yet he also felt sad.
He knew that when he untied Four-legs's rope, the wolf
would run off into the forest. Tall-tree did not like this
thought, but he felt he must set Four-legs free. It was the
only way he could repay the animal for saving his life.

At the cave he knelt, loosened the knot in the leather
rope, and pulled it off Four-legs's neck. The wolf shook
itself and looked at him. Tall-tree turned and went into
the cave. He felt a wetness in his eyes, something he had
not felt since he was a boy. He squatted by the fire and
gathered his weapons for the day's hunt.

Something pattered over the cave floor behind him.
Tall-tree turned. Four-legs stood just inside the cave
opening. Its tail drooped and it held its head low. Its
brown eyes stared into Tall-tree's black ones.

Then the animal moved into the cave. It was a strange movement. Its stomach was on the ground, but the back part of its body was pointed upward. It inched forward with little pulls of its front paws. Slowly it crept toward Tall-tree until its nose was only inches from the man's face. Then it licked Tall-tree's nose.

Tall-tree yelled with delight. Four-legs didn't want to leave; it had said so as plainly as if it could talk! Tall-tree rubbed the animal's head with both hands. Four-legs flopped onto its back, and Tall-tree rubbed its stomach. The wolf's tongue lolled out of its mouth, and its lips were pulled back into what seemed to be a grin as wide as the one on Tall-tree's face.

After a while Tall-tree jumped to his feet. "Come on, Four-legs," he said. "Let's go hunting!"

Four-legs rolled to its feet and shook itself. Then the world's first pet and its two-legged friend hurried off happily together.

279

The Bat

By day the bat is cousin to the mouse.
He likes the attic of an aging house.

His fingers make a hat about his head.
His pulse beat is so slow we think him dead.

He loops in crazy figures half the night
Among the trees that face the corner light.

But when he brushes up against a screen,
We are afraid of what our eyes have seen:

For something is amiss or out of place
When mice with wings can wear a human face.

—Theodore Roethke

Joker

ELIZABETH COATSWORTH

Joker was born on the Circle M ranch in Montana. As a colt he ran with his mother and the other ranch horses in the great pastures at the foot of the mountains. He played with the colts born in his year and learned wisdom from his wise old mother. In the mornings he heard the song of the larks, and at dusk the coyote's howl was his lullaby.

From the beginning Joker was unusually small, round-bodied, and strong. But the remarkable thing about him was his color. Probably there was no other horse in the world quite like him.

On one side he appeared to be a pure white pony with a black tail and a little black cap on the top of his head. But on the other side he seemed all black, with white socks, a white mane, and a milk-white nose. Like his mother, he was a pinto, but instead of being spotted like other pintos, his color was divided in two at the spine.

Mr. Al, the owner of the ranch,

didn't notice Joker until the second summer, when he rode out with a buyer to look over the young stock. "That's a nice-looking white foal over there," the buyer said. Tex, one of the cowboys, cut Joker out from the other horses to join the colts that were going off in the four big trucks. But when the buyer came to look for his white colt, he was nowhere to be found.

"Tex, where's that white colt?" Mr. Al shouted.

Tex grinned and flapped his hat at a black colt that was trying to jump the corral gate. The colt whirled, and there he was! No longer a black colt with a white mane, but a snow-white colt with black trimmings.

"There's a joker," Mr. Al said to the buyer. "You're getting two horses for the price of one."

But to himself he thought, If I had a boy now, I'd save that pony for him.

Mr. Al didn't have a boy, and

281

Mrs. Al said they'd better not go looking for one or they'd make a mistake. In good time a boy would come to them, she said.

"How'll we know he's the right one?" Mr. Al would ask.

"Oh, we'll know," said Mrs. Al. But no boy had come yet.

While the truck with Joker in it moved down the highway by the pasture, Joker's mother followed along the fence, whinnying and whinnying sharp and loud. And from the truck Joker whinnied back to her. She was an old mare and that spring she had no colt, so perhaps she loved Joker all the more.

All day and all night the trucks traveled through strange country, and at last they came to the place where the buyer lived at the edge of a city. And there, in the weeks that followed, the young horses were broken in to harness. The buyer was a patient man and liked horses. Joker and the others were not badly treated. When Joker's education was finished, he was a perfect saddle pony—gentle, intelligent, and strong—with good gaits and a good mouth. If he still remembered pastures—far away where the wild duck rose from the river and an old mare whinnied for her colt—there was no way that anyone would know.

One day in the spring that Joker was two years old, the buyer sold him to Mr. Selwyn, a wealthy man who lived near the country club. Mr. Selwyn wanted to give the pony to his son Ross for a birthday present, and he had paid extra for Joker because of his peculiar coloring.

Ross Selwyn was a show-off, and he didn't know or care much about horses or how they felt. He was delighted with Joker and soon saw how gentle and willing he was.

But Ross wanted to be admired, and he loved to play tricks on people.

As he rode Joker past friends, he would suddenly spin him around, with a dig of a spur, a jerk of the rein, and a slap of the whip. Everyone, suddenly seeing a black pony turn white or a white pony turn black, would laugh and applaud, and Ross would spin Joker around full circle and ride on, all smiles.

But Joker soon dreaded the boy's hand on the rein and his foot in the stirrup. One day the good-natured, well-trained pony ran away and scraped Ross out of the saddle. Someone caught Joker, and when Ross got him home, he took the carriage whip and beat him.

The stableman tried to interfere. "You'll only teach him to kick. He's a good pony if he's rightly treated." But Ross knew better.

"I'll teach you," he kept saying over and over through his teeth, and he did teach Joker. He taught him to rear and buck and bite and strike out with his front feet and lash out with his hind feet. He taught him to fight his rider with all his wit and courage. Very soon, of course, Ross didn't dare ride him at all but used him to play jokes of another kind. When friends came to spend the day with him, Ross would offer to let them ride his pinto, and so round and pretty did Joker look, and so quietly did he stand while he was being saddled, that at first the friends were eager to ride him.

But some he threw at once by bucking, and some later by running under the young oak tree by the drive, and some by shying at the mailbox near the gate, and some by rearing in the road. And then how Ross would laugh!

"I told you his name was Joker," he would say. "Be a sport! The joke's on you."

Soon very few children came to play with Ross, and no one at all would ride Ross's pinto pony. For days Joker stood in the paddock, with only one desire in his heart. He longed to be home again, to be running with the horses of the Circle M ranch while the mountains climbed the sky and the Herefords bawled under the cottonwoods in the wash.

One day there appeared at the Selwyn stable a boy of about fifteen, looking for work. He told the stableman and the gardener that his name was Bill and that he was an orphan raised in the cattle country. His father had died about a month earlier and the bank had taken their place. Bill had a dollar and seventeen cents in the pocket of his blue jeans. It was all he had in the world, though he didn't tell the men that. Nor did he tell them that he'd been looking for work in the city for a week and hadn't found any.

While Bill was talking to the stableman, Ross slid in as quietly as a hunting cat and listened. "Dad'll be home for lunch," he told Bill. "You'd better wait. Say, would you like to ride my pony while you wait?"

Bill shook his head. "Guess not," he said, leaning against the paddock fence with his hands in his jeans pockets. He didn't feel like riding someone else's pony. The bank had taken his.

"Give you a dollar."

Bill needed a dollar but he didn't like Ross. He shook his head.

Ross was accustomed to having his own way. "If you ride the pony, you can have him," he said.

He was sure no one could ride Joker, and he wanted to see this new boy thrown. It would serve him right for not being polite enough to do what he was asked to do.

Bill gave Ross a long look. Then he looked at Joker.

"Throws everyone," the stableman said under his breath. Bill heard him.

"All right. I'll ride him," he said. Ross was delighted.

As usual, Joker stood perfectly quiet while his bridle was put on and the saddle girths tightened. Bill swung into the saddle. Ross began to grin.

But Joker felt something he had not felt for a long time. Someone was sitting on his back who had good balance and a light hand on the rein. A quiet voice spoke to him. He moved forward.

"Hi yah!" shouted Ross, waving his hat, anxious for the fun to begin.

But Joker didn't buck. He didn't sidle under the low branches of the young oak. He didn't shy at the mailbox or rear as he reached the road. Instead, he turned north and broke into an easy lope.

"Here! Come back here!" shouted Ross.

Already Bill was trying to turn Joker's head, but the pony had the bit in his teeth. He was not running away. He was going at an effortless pace, one that he could keep up mile after mile.

"You seem to know where you're going," Bill said to him. "It's more than I can say. Perhaps I'd better just go along with you."

"Stop, thief!" screamed Ross far behind them.

"You said he could have the horse," said the stableman.

"I heard you myself," said the gardener.

"But I never thought he could stay on him," whined Ross.

"Oh, but that pony's a joker!" said the stableman.

"Yes, he sure is a joker!" said the gardener.

On the road leading to the mountains a boy on a two-colored horse was riding toward Circle M ranch, where the eagles swung far up into the sky and Mr. and Mrs. Al waited for the son who someday would come to them, as naturally as an apple grows on an apple tree. The ranch was far away, but a horse will always find the place where he was foaled. Joker had no doubts. He was traveling easily with a light heart. And for the first time since his father's death, Bill's heart was light too, though he scarcely knew why.

He had a horse and a dollar and seventeen cents, and now he could see the mountains in the distance. Everything would be all right.

287

Crickets

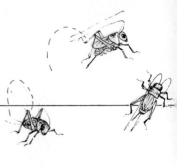

SEYMOUR SIMON

Crickets are easily kept and cared for, interesting to watch, and very musical. A cricket in a jar will start to chirp, usually in the early evening, and keep up a pleasant chorus for hours.

There are several different kinds of crickets in the United States, but you'll most often find the common field cricket. Field crickets live under rocks, boards, decaying logs, in the grass, or almost anywhere on the ground. Watch carefully when a cricket jumps to see where it lands. Then try catching it with your cupped hand or with a net or paper bag. Carefully put the captured cricket into a container.

At home, place some sand at the bottom of a glass jar, along with a few twigs and some leaves. Keep the sand moist but not soggy. Place the cricket in the jar. Be sure you keep the jar covered with screening.

Crickets like shady places out of direct sunlight. They will eat almost any kind of food. Try giving them bits of cut-up potatoes, apples, or some other fruit or vegetable. They will also eat bits of meat. If you feed your crickets some juicy food such as a bit of fruit every day, they will not need any extra water. Or place a piece of moist cotton in the jar. If you don't want to keep watering the cotton every day, you can use a test tube filled with water and plugged with cotton. Just lay the test tube flat on the bottom of the jar.

288

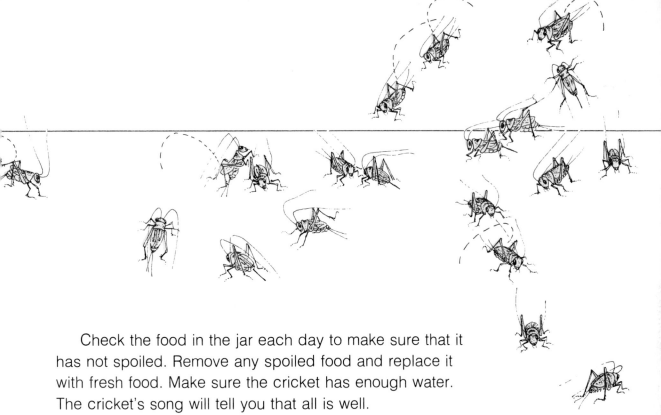

Check the food in the jar each day to make sure that it has not spoiled. Remove any spoiled food and replace it with fresh food. Make sure the cricket has enough water. The cricket's song will tell you that all is well.

Since male crickets fight among themselves, be certain you have only one male in a jar. You can tell a male cricket from a female cricket by comparing the back ends of their bodies. A female cricket has a long tube projecting from the back. The tube is used to lay eggs in the ground. The male cricket has no such tube.

Crickets do not show great physical changes from stage to stage as do other insects, such as butterflies. Cricket eggs are deposited in the soil sometime in the fall and remain there throughout the winter. With the arrival of warmer weather in the spring, the eggs hatch into small crickets called nymphs. The nymphs look much like the adult crickets. The young nymphs feed and grow. When they become too big for their outer skin, the skin splits and a new larger skin forms and hardens. This is called molting. Crickets molt a number of times before they become adults.

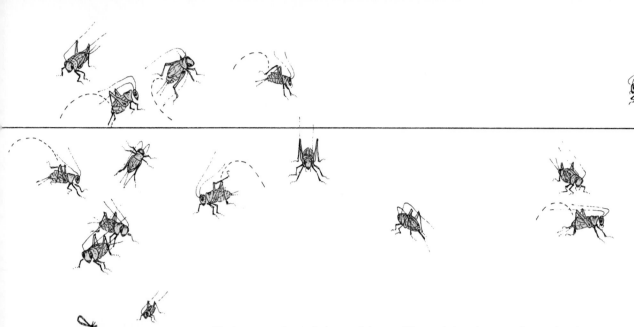

Only a male cricket chirps. The chirp is produced when one wing is drawn across the other. The hard, rough surface on the underside of one wing is pulled across a hardened vein on the upper front of the other wing. The wing vibrates and makes the sound. Most crickets chirp right wing over left wing, but some chirp left wing over right.

The cricket's song is not just for your enjoyment. One kind of chirp is used to attract a female. Another kind is used as a warning to other males. Crickets' songs speed up in warm weather and slow down in cooler weather.

In China and Japan crickets are highly prized for their songs. The cricket is kept in a small bamboo cage so it can be fed and its song heard.

If you have a male and a female cricket in your jar and they mate, the female will lay eggs in the soil. Keep the soil in the jar moist over the winter. If the eggs hatch and nymphs appear in the jar in the spring, feed them the same foods that the adults eat. If you take good care of the nymphs they may repay you with a song when they grow into adults.

The Singing Tortoise

HAROLD COURLANDER
and
GEORGE HERZOG

Far back in the country, near where the Adiri River comes out of the Kong Mountains, a hunter named Ama left his village one day to go hunting. Game was hard to find, and he went deeper and deeper into the forest looking for it. He came to the edge of the river in a part of the forest he had never seen before, and while he stood thinking where to go, he heard music coming from among the trees. He heard a voice singing and the faint tinkling of a *sansa*, which is a kind of tiny piano played with the thumbs. The voice was singing:

> "It is man who imposes himself upon things,
>   Not things which impose themselves upon man."

Ama moved forward quietly and peered through the trees, and there, sitting in a little clearing in the forest, was a tortoise with a *sansa* in her hands. She sang:

> "It is man who imposes himself upon things,
>   Not things which impose themselves upon man."

Ama was astounded. The tortoise sang beautifully. Never had such a thing been heard of in his country. He stood and listened. The tortoise was not afraid but continued to sing and play. The music was as entrancing as anything Ama had ever heard.

He went back to his village after a while, but he couldn't forget the tortoise. The next time he went hunting in the forest, he made his way again to the clearing, and there again he found the tortoise with her *sansa* and heard her sing:

"It is man who imposes himself upon things,
  Not things which impose themselves upon man."

Every time that Ama was in the forest, he went to hear the tortoise, for she was a strange and wonderful thing. And then one day he thought how fine it would be if he had the tortoise in his house in the village so that he could hear her sing at night when he came home from hunting or working his fields. He spoke to the tortoise and asked her if he might take her back with him.

"But this thing is a secret," the tortoise said. "If you took me back with you, people would get to know about it."

"No," Ama said. "If I had you in my house, I would tell no one. It is only I who would hear you."

"If that is true, I'll go back with you," the tortoise said. "But I shall sing only for you, and the people of your village mustn't know."

"No," Ama said happily, "you shall sing just for me!"

He picked the tortoise up with great care so that he wouldn't hurt her and carried her back to his house. And there each night when Ama came in from the fields or from the hunt, the tortoise played her *sansa* and sang to him.

Yet it was such a wonderful thing that Ama couldn't keep from speaking about it to people in the village. He talked about it more and more. Among themselves the people ridiculed Ama for telling such a fantastic tale. No one really believed him. The story of Ama's singing tortoise spread farther and farther, and one day it reached the ears of the chief.

"Who is this man who pretends to have a singing tortoise?" the chief said. "He will bring ridicule upon us with this silly story." And the chief sent messengers to Ama to tell him to come to his house.

When Ama came the chief sat upon his stool in his courtyard, with his councilors standing by, and listened to the tale. Ama felt proud and important to own the thing that was causing so much excitement in the district.

But the chief was disturbed, and the councilors shook their heads and were scornful of what Ama told them. "There's no such thing as a singing tortoise," they said, "or a tortoise that can play a *sansa*."

"Everything I have told you is the way it happened," Ama said.

"You are impudent," the people said. "You are bringing disgrace upon us with your nonsensical talk."

Ama's feelings were hurt, and he said, "I'll bring the tortoise here. She will sing and play for you. If she can't do this, then you may beat me for it!"

He went back to his village. Everyone was talking about Ama and his tortoise. He picked her up carefully and started off.

"Where are we going?" the tortoise asked.

"The people think I am lying," Ama said. "We'll show them!" The tortoise said nothing.

When Ama came to the chief's house, there was a great crowd around it, for people had come from all the nearby villages to see what would happen. Ama placed the tortoise on the ground and put her *sansa* beside her.

293

"Now you will see," he said.

The tortoise stayed quietly where Ama had placed her, and the people pushed close in a circle to see. But the tortoise didn't sing, nor did she pick up the *sansa*. The people waited. Nothing happened. The people argued among themselves. They became impatient. Minutes passed by. The tortoise pulled her head into her shell. Sometimes she put her head out to look at the people, and then she would pull it in again. Finally the people became angry.

294

"Well, when is she going to sing?" they asked.

"Sing for them so they will see I am not a liar," Ama said to the tortoise. But the tortoise only blinked her eyes. Time passed. People began to say angry things to Ama.

At last the chief said, "Well, we have seen. This man Ama has ridiculed us with his story. Now take him and beat him for it."

So the people took Ama where he stood and beat him hard with sticks. They beat him a long time, until the chief told them to stop.

"This will teach you not to bring a bad name to our people by lying," the chief said. "Now pack your things and leave the village, for we have no room for such troublemakers."

Ama said nothing. His body ached, and he was overcome with shame. He took his possessions and left the village. The people watched him until he was out of sight.

At this moment the tortoise put her head out of her shell and spoke. The people looked in wonder.

"Ama earned his shame through bad faith," the tortoise said. "He brought his punishment upon himself. I was happy in the forest singing and playing my *sansa*. Then he brought me to his house, promising to keep my secret. But he couldn't keep it. He told it to all the world, first in whispers, then with a loud voice."

Then she picked up her little *sansa* and sang once more:

> "It is man who imposes himself upon things,
> Not things which impose themselves upon man."

A Name for a Kitten

A Folk Tale from Vietnam

Retold by BEATRICE TANAKA

No one knows whether the King's kitten was white, black, or striped. But history says His Majesty was so fond of his pet that he asked the royal council to choose a name for it.

"I want a very strong, powerful, and honorable name for my dearest kitten," he said. "So I propose to call it Sky because the sky is above everything and everyone on earth!"

"That is a most noble name, indeed!" said his Prime Mandarin. "But though the sky is above the clouds, the clouds sometimes dare to hide its blue beauty."

"A very interesting observation!" praised the King. "Clouds, though lower than the sky, can be more powerful. I want my pet to have an extraordinarily strong name. I will call it Cloud."

"What a lovely name!" said the Chief Magician. "But is it really strong? The wind scatters the clouds and sometimes even pushes them across the sea and beyond the horizon."

"True, very true," said the King. "And since the wind is more powerful than the clouds which, though lower than the sky dare to hide its blue beauty, I'll call my darling Wind."

"A most fit name for a prancing, running kitten," said the King's General. "But is wind as powerful as the Magician suggests? A high, solid wall can bar the wind."

"A wall? I didn't think of that, but now that you mention it—of course you're right, General! A wall stops the wind which scatters the clouds which hide the sky. Wall! That's a fine, strong name!"

"Is it really?" wondered the King's Steward. "Only yesterday the thick eastern wall of Your Majesty's garden tumbled down."

"How horrible!" said the King. "Happily the name Wall wasn't yet officially proclaimed! And what made it tumble down?"

"Mice," said the Steward.

"Mice? I didn't realize they were more powerful than the wall which stops the wind which scatters the clouds which hide the sky. I'll call my dearest pet Mouse," said the King.

"But any cat eats mice!" exclaimed the little servant girl, who was preparing tea for the royal council.

"How strange! How wonderful! And who eats cats?" said the King, quite forgetting that according to court etiquette servant girls shouldn't open their mouths.

"Why, nobody, Sir!" laughed the little girl.

"In that case the extraordinarily strong and powerful name we wanted for the Royal Kitten has been found!" declared the King. "Gentlemen, I hereby most solemnly and officially name it Cat!"

And that's how kittens came to have the extraordinary name of "cat" right up to the present day!

297

Pangur Bán

*Written by a student of the
monastery of Carinthia
on a copy of St. Paul's Epistles,
in the eighth century*

I and Pangur Bán, my cat,
'Tis a like task we are at;
Hunting mice is his delight,
Hunting words I sit all night.

Better far than praise of men
'Tis to sit with book and pen;
Pangur bears me no ill-will,
He too plies his simple skill.

'Tis a merry thing to see
At our tasks how glad are we,
When at home we sit and find
Entertainment to our mind.

Oftentimes a mouse will stray
In the hero Pangur's way;
Oftentimes my keen thought set
Takes a meaning in its net.

'Gainst the wall he sets his eye
Full and fierce and sharp and sly;
'Gainst the wall of knowledge I
All my little wisdom try.

When a mouse darts from its den,
O how glad is Pangur then!
O what gladness do I prove
When I solve the doubts I love!

So in peace our tasks we ply,
Pangur Bán, my cat, and I;
In our arts we find our bliss,
I have mine and he has his.

Practice every day has made
Pangur perfect in his trade;
I get wisdom day and night
Turning darkness into light.

Anon: *translated from the Gaelic by* Robin Flower

299

Janet Reachfar and Chickabird

JANE DUNCAN

It was a beautiful bright spring morning on the Reachfar farm in the Highlands of Scotland. But Janet, who lived there, was in the most terrible temper. Just after breakfast she had run up the farmyard to the moor gate. But before she could climb over the gate, she heard a voice calling, "Janet, come back here this minute!" It was the voice of her grandmother being the stern person that Janet and her friends George and Tom called "Herself." Janet came slowly back down the yard.

"You are not going to run around the moor like a wild hare today," Herself said. "You are a person and not a hare, and people have work to do. Go and lead the horses out of the stable and put them in the west field."

Janet liked her grandmother and all her family and all the animals of Reachfar, but now she felt that she did not

like any of them. She wanted to be out on the moor that morning and not helping around the farmyard. But she had to do what Herself said.

She led Betsy from the stable, then Dulcie, then went back for Dick. He was very big and very good-natured, but on this morning he seemed to be feeling a little wild too. As Janet led him out, he danced about on his big hooves, tossing his huge head, and tried to turn the wrong way at the stable door.

"Stop your nonsense, you silly big thing!" Janet said crossly, slapping him on the nose.

People did not as a rule call Dick silly and slap him, and he was so startled that he did something he had never done before. He went jumping backwards and stepped on a half-grown chicken and broke its leg.

Janet felt her bad temper running out through the tips of her toes as George picked up the chicken. "We'll have to kill this bird," he said.

"That is one of the early flock," Tom told him. He turned to Janet. "What were you thinking of, slapping Dick like that?"

Janet began to cry. "Don't kill it!" she said. "Please don't kill it!"

"Stop crying," George told her. "Go and put Dick in the field and come back to the barn."

When she got back, George was sitting on a heap of sacks holding the chicken while he and Tom looked at it sadly. "We'll have to kill it, Janet," Tom said. "The other grown-up hens will kill it anyway. Birds and animals do not like sick members of the flock."

Janet felt terrible. She felt that she had killed the chicken. It had been hurt because of her temper.

"Stop worrying!" George told her. "Run along to the house and see what Herself is doing."

Janet knew that now George was not going to kill the chicken. He was going to try to make its leg better. She ran to the house and back to the barn. "Granny is busy baking," she said.

"Good," said George. "Tom, get me a little piece of wood to make a splint, and Janet, you tear up your handkerchief. If Herself notices that it is gone, you'll get a scolding, but you deserve a scolding today anyhow."

Tom and Janet did as George told them, and very soon he had put a little wooden splint on the chicken's leg. Then he handed the bird to Janet.

"You will have to take care of her," he said. "The other hens won't like this splint. It isn't natural for a chicken to have a wooden leg. You had better take a coop up to the moor and hide her there, and let's hope Herself doesn't notice that one of the flock is missing. But remember, Janet, the leg may not get better. I have never put a splint on a chicken before.''

"It will get better," Janet said. "It will! It will!''

So Janet hid the chicken on the moor, and for a whole month she took great care of her. She named her Chickabird, and carried food secretly to her, wishing and hoping hard all the time that the leg would get better. Then one Sunday George examined the leg and said, "I think it has mended. We can take the splint off.''

Chickabird had grown into quite a big fat brown hen, with a tuft of feathers on top of her head that was a little like Herself's best hat. At first the leg was too weak to hold her up, but soon it grew perfectly strong.

But Chickabird had grown accustomed to her coop on the moor and would not come down to the farmyard to be with the other hens or sleep in the henhouse at night. She stayed on the moor by herself, pecking around and growing bigger and fatter and shinier every day.

"When the snow comes she will be glad to come down to the henhouse," Tom said.

Janet thought so, too, for when the winter snow lay deep, wild creatures came down from the moor in search of food—creatures that were never seen near the Reachfar house in the summertime.

But when the snow came, Chickabird did not come down. She clucked around her coop, watched the roe deer eat the hay that George, Tom, and Janet put out for them, and cocked her head at the big curlew who came poking about for worms in the mud and slush around the

moor pond. She behaved as if she were a very special hen and all the wild creatures were her guests. And Janet gave her much more corn than the other hens so that she would have some to spare for any guests who wanted it, like the ugly big black crow that perched on top of her coop.

One morning around Christmas time, when the snow was very deep, Janet went up to the moor with some corn and found that Chickabird had a very special guest. Pecking around in the snow beside her was a beautiful cock pheasant with his long tail feathers shining against the snow, the greenish feathers on his neck gleaming. When his fierce wild eye saw Janet he flew away with a loud whirr of his wings. But after that he was there every morning and afternoon, sharing Chickabird's corn. Janet hoped that he would grow tame and stay at Reachfar, but George and Tom said that this would not happen.

"He is wild by nature," George said, "and when spring comes, he will go back to the wild part of the moor."

They were right. One morning, after the snow was gone, Janet went up to the moor with her basket of corn, and the pheasant was gone. But worse, Chickabird was gone too. Janet called and called her, but she did not come.

"A weasel must have gotten her," Tom said.

"Or that fox your father saw in the glen last week," said George. "It was stupid of us to let her stay up there by herself. Tame creatures can't defend themselves in the wild."

"We couldn't help it!" Janet cried. "She wouldn't stay in the yard."

By Easter time Janet had almost forgotten about
Chickabird, though the coop still sat among the gorse
bushes. On Easter Sunday Janet decided that she and Fly,
her dog, would walk over the moor to see how many
wild primroses were in bloom. As they passed the coop,
there came from inside it a comfortable clucking noise,
then a high cheep-cheeping noise, and a tiny
yellowish-brown chicken ran out and back again.

Janet peered in and saw a wonderful sight. There was
Chickabird. She stood up, fluffed out her feathers so that
she looked very fat, and stepped aside proudly to show
Janet her flock of baby chicks. Janet counted twelve of
them altogether. But they were not quite like the other
yellow chickens down in the farmyard. They were
different in the way that the pheasant was different from
the hens in the farmyard and the wild flowers of the
moor were different from the flowers in the garden.

Suddenly, out of the heather, the cock pheasant rose, flew fast over the coop, his long tail streaming, and away up toward the far part of the moor, calling in his wild harsh voice as he went.

All Janet's family came to see Chickabird and her family. Herself looked very hard at the coop in the gorse, and then she looked at George and Tom. "It is a strange thing for a Reachfar hen to wish to live on this wild moor," she said. But then she turned into Janet's wise kind Granny as she said to Janet, "It was clever of Chickabird to bring her children back. But they are only half wild, and she needs you to help her bring them up."

After that, Janet carried food to the coop several times a day, for like their mother, Chickabird's chicks did not want to come down to the farmyard. They preferred to stay up on the moor.

"I like them better than the farmyard chickens," Janet told her mother one night. "Do you like them?"

"Yes. I like wild things. Perhaps that is why I like a certain girl who sometimes runs wild on the moor, even though she comes back for meals in the Reachfar kitchen," her mother teased.

Reindeer

CARROLL LANE FENTON
and
HERMINIE B. KITCHEN

A herd of reindeer walked across a rolling plain in Lapland. In a few places the ground was bare, but most of it was covered with snow. The deer's hoofs left broad, curved tracks as the animals walked across the snow.

Most deer are wild animals, but these reindeer were domesticated. They belonged to two families of people called Lapps. The Lapps had spent the winter in wooden houses near the edge of a forest, where the deer were sheltered from storms. But when spring came the people left their houses and began to travel northward. They were taking the deer to their summer pasture near the shore of the Arctic Ocean.

Many deer had nothing to do but walk. Others carried packs that were tied to their backs. Still other deer pulled boat-shaped sleds, which the Lapps call "pulkas." Some pulkas were piled high with tents, bedding, pots for cooking and for coffee, and other household goods. Other pulkas carried women with babies, and some grandfathers and grandmothers who could not walk very far. Children with red coats and woolen caps ran beside the sleds. Men and big boys with dogs followed the herd to keep the deer from lagging or wandering away on the plain.

In the Far North, when summer draws near, the sun rises above the horizon and does not set for weeks. At first the sunshine is dull and cool, but it soon becomes brighter

308

309

and warmer. At last it begins to melt the snow. This uncovers bushes and other small plants that grow close to the ground.

The man who was leader of the Lapps kept watch for a broad southern slope on which most of the snow had melted. When he saw one, he pointed to it and shouted some words that meant, "This is the place to stop!" The other men answered, "All right," and began to turn the reindeer. When the animals came to the plant-covered slope, they began to feed.

Many deer feed on grass and the tender tips of bushes. Reindeer like these things too, but their favorite food is a bluish-gray plant known as reindeer moss. It really is a lichen, related to the thin, dry lichens that grow on rocks and trees.

While the deer munched their moss, the Lapp women put up tents, made beds on the ground, and began to cook. The men selected milking deer from the herd so the children could have milk with their meal. After supper the grandparents told stories, and then almost everyone went to bed. Only a few men and older boys stayed awake to watch over the reindeer and keep them from wandering away.

Reindeer now live in cold regions on the tundra from Norway to Siberia and from islands in the Arctic Ocean to Eastern Russia. Many also live in woods among high mountains. They thrive in the forests of the Ural Mountains and in the region around Lake Baykal in southern Siberia. Long ago, during the Ice Age, the deer ranged across Germany and into southern France. There they were killed and eaten by Stone-Age hunters who lived in shallow caves. Some of these hunters also painted pictures of the deer, just as they painted pictures of horses, bison, cattle, and other wild animals.

Although ancient hunters of France killed reindeer, they did not domesticate the animals. This was probably done first by the Samoyeds, a Siberian-Mongolian people in the Baykal area. These people trained the deer as they did horses and cattle and used them for riding, pack, and draft animals. They probably took domesticated forest deer to Europe, where they developed into the tundra deer of the modern Lapps.

In China, by the end of the fifth century, domesticated reindeer were being driven and milked. The Norse people of the ninth century left records of tame deer. And before the tenth century domestic reindeer were drawing sleds

311

carrying three or four persons in the area southeast of Lake Baykal. People there made clothes of the animal skins.

Today the Lapps depend on their reindeer for meat, milk, cheese, and skins. The wealth of these people is determined by the number of deer owned. In Finland, reindeer meat is considered a great delicacy and brings a high price.

Wild reindeer grow four to five feet high at the shoulder and weigh as much as 300 pounds. They have heavy bodies and rather short legs, with broad hoofs and hairy feet that do not sink into the snow. The nose is covered with soft furry hair, and coarse hair on neck and body covers a wooly undercoat. The head and neck are almost white, but the rest of the coat is brownish gray and brown.

Both male and female reindeer have antlers. Those of the female are small, but the male's antlers grow large and branch several times. The strongest, healthiest deer have the largest antlers.

Most domestic reindeer are smaller than wild ones, though they are strong enough to pull loads of 300 pounds at eight to ten miles an hour. One special breed raised in Siberia is larger than domestic reindeer of Europe. This big deer is more often ridden than hitched to a sled.

Wild reindeer of North America are known as caribou. Caribou of several kinds once ranged from Alaska to Newfoundland, and from Greenland to Idaho and Wisconsin. In many places they have been killed by hunters. But there still are large herds in Alaska and northern Canada.

Besides caribou, a few herds of domestic reindeer now live in Alaska. They are descendants of animals brought from Siberia by the United States government, which hired Lapp herders to teach Eskimos to care for the animals. For a time the herds were handled with some success, but by 1969 only 30,000 domestic reindeer were left in western Alaska.

In 1929 the Canadian government bought 3,000 Alaskan reindeer to provide food and clothing for Eskimos in the Northwest Territories. These people also were trained to take care of the deer by herders who came from Lapland.

The only other country in which reindeer are kept is Iceland. The animals were taken there in 1870. They have done very well, although the climate is much warmer than the climate of Lapland, northern Alaska, or northwestern Canada.

The Bulls of Altamira

WILLIAM H. HOOKS

Maria Sautuola and her father, Don Marcelino, had looked forward to exploring the cave at Altamira, near the family's country house. Then one day Don Marcelino found a Stone Age needle in the cave. In the weeks that followed, he and Maria went to the cave many times. There were good days when something turned up and they would shout, "What luck!" But many days the floor of the cave yielded nothing at all.

Once Papa asked, "Wouldn't you rather stay home, Maria? Aren't you getting bored with all this?"

"No, Papa," Maria protested. "I love working in the cave with you. Every time we come to the cave, I think, Today we are going to find something special. I don't even know what the special thing could be. It's just a feeling I have." She wavered. "That must sound silly."

"Silly? Let me make a confession. That's the same way I feel."

They laughed and Papa said no more about going to the cave alone.

The collection of Stone Age things grew slowly. Besides the long needle and a necklace there were several stone ax heads, a few spear points, some flint scrapers, a bone knife, and a horn javelin.

Several times Papa said, "Soon I must take our finds from the cave to Professor Villanova." But he kept putting off the trip back to Madrid. "In a few days," he would say. But finally he told Mama, "I want to make one more trip to the cave, then we'll leave."

As they rode to the cave the next morning, Maria felt a sadness come over her. This could be the last time she and Papa would ever visit the cave. They still hadn't found the special thing she always felt was going to turn up. And when they returned to Madrid, Papa would be gone all day, taking care of business.

Inside the cave, Maria was restless. She wandered slowly around the large entrance chamber, looking at each section of the familiar room

as if saying good-bye. She passed the dark passageway at the back of the room and remembered Papa's Rule Number 1—You must not wander into any part of the cave unless I am with you. Soon she was near the pile of rocks which partly concealed the dark side room which she and Papa had once briefly explored. The wind made a low whistling sound as she walked by. Maria shivered, remembering how strange she had felt in that mysterious room. For the first time she felt a strong urge to visit it again. She quickly walked over to where the box of candles was lying, picked one up, and lighted it.

The candle sputtered as Maria approached the rock-strewn entrance. She cupped it with her hand and pushed on into the pitch-black chamber. The candlelight sent wild, jagged shadows fleeing around the walls. The same chill and dampness which Maria remembered from the first visit surrounded her. Slowly she examined the floor for holes. Then

315

she circled the walls with her candle, examined more of the floor, and moved on. In this manner she soon had the plan of the room figured out. It was about twice as long as it was wide. Although the ceiling was low, she could stand upright in all but the far end, where the ceiling sloped down close to the floor.

She felt more at ease. At least the room didn't have underground streams or deep holes. She sat for a moment on a rock and began moving the candle around the walls, watching it make shapes like fantastic creatures as it bounced from one surface to another. She began to enjoy the game. Soon she was making up names for some of the shapes: a monster bat, a cloud of bees, a flaming tiger. She played with the tiger shape, making it leap from rock to rock. Suddenly she swept the candle across the ceiling. Her arm froze in midair.

A great eye was staring directly at her! This was no make-believe tiger. It was a real eye, looking straight at her from the ceiling. The candle trembled in her hand. Her mouth moved, but no sound came from her throat. She tilted the candle a little

to one side. The staring eye was set in a great shaggy head. Somehow she managed to move her arm enough to see the whole shape. It looked like a huge bull charging from above. Maria circled the candle further along the ceiling. Another bull! And another! She found her voice.

"Bulls! Bulls! Bulls!" she cried.

Papa heard. "Maria! Where are you?" he shouted.

He ran toward the entrance, thinking Maria had seen a stray bull outside the cave.

"Bulls! Bulls!" Maria shouted again.

Papa turned back. The sound was coming from inside the cave. He stumbled across to the rocks and crawled through the dark entrance to the room where Maria was.

"Papa! Papa! Look! Bulls!"

She was pointing toward the ceiling. He dropped to his knees to comfort her. From his knees he could look up at the ceiling.

"Bulls!" Maria whispered. She raised the candle, and it was Papa's turn to become speechless. The great eye stared down at him. It seemed to blink as the candle flickered.

Papa reached for the candle and

began moving it around the ceiling. More and more animals appeared. The ceiling was covered with a great herd of them.

Finally Papa spoke. "Maria, this cannot be." His voice quickened. "For thousands of years this cave has been sealed. Who could have done these paintings? Come, let's get more candles. We must take a better look."

Papa was already scrambling toward the passageway. Maria followed. They lit several candles and returned quickly. With the additional candlelight they could see larger portions of the ceiling. The painted animals looked alive. Some were running and galloping; others were standing still or asleep. The one with the great eye which had first stared out of the ceiling at Maria looked like a huge wounded bull. His head was pulled down and his hind legs were buckling underneath him.

"They look like they were just painted," said Maria. "The colors are so fresh. They look like they're still wet."

Papa reached up and touched one of the animals. He pulled his hand back into the candlelight. His fingers looked bloody! They were smeared with red paint.

"They are wet, Maria. The paint comes off when you touch it!" Then Papa said again, "This cannot be."

He studied the ceiling for a long time. He was so intent that Maria did not try to talk. Instead, she tried counting the animals in the big scene. It was hard because some of them were painted over parts of others. She counted more than twenty. They were mostly bulls, but there were also some deer, a couple of horses, a wolf, and three animals that looked like pigs. As she studied the animals, Maria realized that the bulls looked different from any she had ever seen before.

"Papa, these are strange-looking bulls. What kind are they?"

"I've been thinking the same thing, Maria. They're not bulls at all. They're bison. And no bison have been seen in this part of the world for thousands of years." Then he muttered again, "This cannot be."

This time Maria responded to Papa's strange remark. "But, Papa, it is. The paintings are real. What do you mean, this cannot be?"

"Maria, I will say this only for your ears—anyone else would think I'm crazy. I believe you have discovered the first Stone Age paintings any living person has ever seen. If they were really painted thousands of years ago, this discovery will change our thinking about Stone Age people. This is not the work of unskilled savages."

Papa sounded very solemn. And yet Maria could feel the excitement in his voice.

"Come, Maria. Quickly, let's get packed. We're going home. I must send a message to Professor Villanova. It won't be necessary to take my finds from the cave to Madrid. The professor will come to us now. How could he resist?"

On the way home, Maria and Papa were silent. They were still overwhelmed by the discovery of the paintings. Papa finally spoke.

"Do you know what date today is, Maria?"

"Yes, Papa. It is the eighteenth of November, 1879."

"Remember that date, Maria. It could be the most important date in your life."

A short time afterward, Professor Villanova publicly announced the discoveries at a lecture in the city of Santander. He described the cave of Altamira and the paintings on the ceilings and walls. The tools, weapons, and jewelry Maria and Papa found in the cave were displayed. Professor Villanova showed the ocher crayons, the bowls, and the hollow bones with traces of paint on them that the Sautuolas had found later. He explained why he was sure the paintings were done by Stone Age artists.

The professor pointed out that the cave had been sealed airtight for thousands of years and was protected from damage by people. The cave also remained at a constant temperature, which helped preserve the pictures. The paintings were done in mineral colors which would last indefinitely. They were hidden in total darkness which would keep the colors from fading. There was no noise which might cause cracks in the paintings. And, finally, over the centuries the paintings had become coated with calcite which acted as a clear protective covering.

At the end of the lecture, the

professor introduced Don Marcelino, who told about his work in the cave. Then, after Don Marcelino had spoken, the professor said to the audience, "My good friends, I have saved the best for the last. I would like to present to you the one who discovered the first Stone Age paintings ever seen by any living person—Señorita Maria de Sautuola!"

Maria stood up and curtsied to the audience. The crowd cheered.

After the lecture a trickle of local people began to visit the cave. The large newspapers sent more reporters to Altamira, and stories began to appear in Spain and other countries. Maria was the center of attention. Everyone asked to see and talk to the young girl who had made the famous discovery.

But archaeologists would not come to Altamira. They believed that the paintings were fakes. Don Marcelino spent the rest of his life trying to prove that the cave

paintings of Altamira were the work of Stone Age artists. With Maria's help he wrote a book about the paintings. But no one took it seriously. In 1888, when Maria was eighteen years old, her father died, broken and discredited.

In the late 1890s several caves in the south of France were explored, and paintings like the ones at Altamira were discovered. Maria wrote to the leading archaeologists and asked them to come see the cave at Altamira. Finally in 1902, over twenty years after Maria first made her discovery, archaeologists examined the cave at Altamira and acknowledged that the paintings were genuine examples of Stone Age art.

In 1947, carbon dating, a scientific method for determining the age of objects, was perfected. The method was applied to the paintings of Altamira. They proved to be at least 15,000 years old.

Cluster 7

The Southpaw

JUDITH VIORST

Dear Richard,
Don't invite me to your birthday party because I'm not coming.
And give me back the Disney land sweatshirt I said you could wear.
If I'm not good enough to play on your team, I'm not good enough to be friends with.
　　　　　　Your former friend,
　　　　　　　　Janet
P.S. I hope when you go to the dentist he finds 20 cavities.

Dear Janet,

Here is your stupid Disneyland sweatshirt, if that's how you're going to be. I want my comic books now— finished or not. No girl has ever played on the Mapes Street baseball team, and as long as I'm captain, no girl ever will.

　　　　Your former friend.
　　　　　Richard

P.S. I hope when you go for your checkup you need a tetanus shot.

Dear Richard,
I'm changing my goldfish's name
from Richard to Stanley. Don't count
on my vote for class president next
year. Just because I'm a member of
the ballet club doesn't mean
I'm not a terrific ball player.

                    Your former friend,
                    Janet
P.S. I see you lost your first game, 28-0.

Dear Janet,

I'm not saving any more
seats for you on the bus.
For all I care you can
stand the whole way
to school. Why ~~don't~~ don't
you just forget about
baseball and learn something
nice, like knitting?

            Your former friend,
            Richard

P.S. Wait until
Wednesday.

323

Dear Richard,
 My father said I could call someone
to go with us for a ride and
hot fudge Sundaes. In case you didn't
notice, I didn't call you.

                    Your former friend,
                    Janet

P.S. I see you lost your second game, 34-0.

Dear Janet,

Remember when I took the laces
out of my blue-and-white
sneakers and gave them to you?
I want them back.
                    Your former friend,
                    Richard
P.S. Wait until Friday.

Dear Richard,
 Congratulations on your
unbroken record. Eight straight
losses, wow! I understand you're
the laughing stock of New Jersey.

                    Your former friend,
                    Janet

P.S. Why don't you and your team
forget about baseball and learn something nice like knitting maybe?

Dear Janet,

Here's the silver horseback riding trophy that you gave me. I don't think I want to keep it anymore.

Your former friend,
Richard

P.S. I didn't think you'd be the kind who'd kick a man when he's down.

Dear Richard,
I wasn't kicking exactly. I was kicking back.

Your former friend,
Janet

P.S. In case you were wondering, my batting average is .345.

Dear Janet,

Alfie is having his tonsils out tomorrow. We might be able to let you catch next week.

Richard

Dear Richard,
I pitch.

Janet

Dear Janet,

Joel is moving to Kansas and Danny sprained his wrist. How about a permanent place in the outfield?

Richard

Dear Richard,
I pitch.

Janet

325

Dear Janet,

Ronnie caught the chicken pox
and Leo broke his toe and Elwood
has these stupid violin lessons. I'll
give you first base, and that's my
final offer.
                    Richard

Dear Richard,
  Susan Reilly plays first base,
  Marilyn Jackson catches, Ethel Kahn
  plays center field, I pitch. It's a package
deal.   Janet

P.S. Sorry about your 12-game losing streak.

Dear Janet,
  Please! Not Marilyn Jackson.   Richard

Dear Richard,
Nobody ever said that I
was unreasonable. How about
Lizzie Martindale instead?
                    Janet

Dear Janet,
   At least could you call your
goldfish Richard again?
                    Richard

326

The King of Soccer

CLARE and FRANK GAULT

A small boy danced barefoot out into the street and began kicking at the air as if he were kicking a soccer ball. But there was no ball. Nearby, a group of men and boys huddled around a radio, listening to a local soccer game: Bauru against São Carlos, a neighboring town in southeastern Brazil. The year was 1948.

One of the men smiled as he watched the boy acting like a real soccer player. The boy was eight years old. His name was Edson Arantes Do Nacimento, but his friends called him Pelé (pronounced *pay*-lay).

Pelé kept kicking at the air. He could imagine himself out on the soccer field, dribbling the ball downfield with his feet, passing it to a teammate, then taking a pass in return and kicking a goal.

Suddenly, the radio announcer became excited. Bauru had the ball near the São Carlos goal. Pelé stopped to listen. A player nicknamed Dondinho was moving in to take a shot, and it looked as if he would score. Dondinho kicked, but he missed. Everybody groaned.

Dondinho was one of the policemen in town, but he played soccer part-time for the local club to earn a little extra money for his family. He was also Pelé's father. Pelé ran home. Soon his father arrived too, looking very sad.

Pelé's mother said, "See what that game does to you. You missed a goal, and now you'll be sad for days. I pray Pelé never plays soccer." But that night, when Pelé's father, mother, grandmother, younger brother, and sister gathered for prayers, Pelé prayed he would become a great soccer player.

The next morning Pelé dressed to go to school. He put his lunch in a paper bag. He put in his soccer ball too—one of his father's old socks stuffed hard with newspapers and laced shut with string. It was no bigger than a large orange and not very round, but it was the only soccer ball Pelé had. He had no money to buy a real one.

Pelé took his soccer ball everywhere. He would practice kicking it as he walked down the street. He would dribble it. Or aim it at a telephone pole. He could do almost anything with it.

Pelé often went to the field behind the town's soccer stadium. He could usually get in on a game there. The

games were a lot of fun. But after a while, Pelé felt he was missing something. He wanted his own team that could play other teams on a regular soccer field with a real ball.

"If we had uniforms," he told his friends, "other teams would play us as a team. We could call ourselves the Seventh of September." (The seventh of September is Brazil's Independence Day.)

To get money for uniforms, the boys collected old bottles and anything else they could find. They went up and down the streets and alleys. They poked into trash cans. They raked the city dump. When they had a big pile of old bottles, scrap metal, pieces of pipe, and old pieces of furniture, they took it all to a junk man to sell. Finally they had scraped together enough money to buy shirts and pants, but not enough for shoes and socks.

"We'll just have to be known as Seventh of September, the barefoot team," said Pelé.

The Seventh of September played every other team they could, and in time they became famous in the area. When Pelé was about eleven years old, the mayor of Bauru decided to hold a big tournament for all the younger teams. It was to be held in the city stadium with professional referees, just like big-league soccer.

Pelé and his friends wanted to enter the tournament, but they needed new uniforms. This time, a traveling salesman helped them. He was a soccer fan and had heard of the barefoot team. He put up the money for uniforms, socks, and shoes. However, he asked that the team be called Little America after his favorite big-league team, America, in Rio de Janeiro.

That seemed to be a small price to pay. As soon as their equipment came, the boys started to practice. But after only a few minutes they were unhappy. They had never played in shoes before.

"I can't feel the ball," Pelé said. "I kick it, but it won't go where I want it to."

So they all took off their shoes and went back to playing barefoot. One of the tournament officials saw them. "Boys, you have to wear shoes in the games, so you might as well get used to them. Without shoes you can't play."

The boys had no choice but to

put their shoes back on. They got blisters the first day, but after a few days the shoes became more comfortable. And Pelé began to get the feel of the ball. He found he could kick with his toes as well as with the sides of his feet. The ball traveled farther with less effort. Wearing shoes is better, he finally decided.

Sixteen teams entered the tournament. Little America won their first game; then they won their second game and their third. Suddenly they were in the finals, playing for the championship before a huge crowd.

329

It was a hard, close game, but years of playing together paid off. Pelé was especially good that day, dribbling, passing, and shooting all over the field.

Late in the game, Pelé got the ball and dribbled it quickly toward the goal. An opposing player moved in to take the ball away. Suddenly, Pelé stopped cold and changed direction, still controlling the ball with his feet. The other player tried to change direction too, but he slipped and fell to the ground.

In a flash, Pelé was racing for the goal. Only the goalkeeper was in his way now. Out from the net came the goalie to try to smother the ball. Pelé faked a kick. The goalie dove, but the ball wasn't where he thought it would be. Pelé angled a soft shot for the corner of the net. Bounce. Bounce. The goalie raced for it. But it went into the net. It was a goal.

The crowd stood and cheered. Little America had won. The crowd started to chant, *"Pelé, Pelé, Pelé."* Pelé heard his name and ran around the field, his arms raised in victory. The people threw coins out onto the field. They added up to $3.50, more money than he had ever seen before.

A few days later, Pelé's father found him sitting behind the fence in back of the house, thinking about the victory and smoking a cigarette.

His father looked at him for a minute and then said, "How long have you been smoking?"

"Not long," answered Pelé. "Only a few days."

"Do you enjoy it?" his father asked.

"Not really. I just thought I'd try it," Pelé said.

"Well," said his father, "cigarettes will cut down on your wind, and nobody needs wind like a soccer player. If you want to be a great player, you'll protect your body." He turned and went back into the house.

Pelé put the cigarette out and threw the others into the trash can.

He never smoked again.

When Pelé was fifteen years old, a big-league team named after a large port city in Brazil, Santos, signed him to a contract. For the first time he was to be paid for playing soccer. Pelé started with the junior Santos team. He practiced and played with them for three months before he got his chance to play with the Santos first team. He entered an exhibition game as center forward in the second half and scored his first goal in big-league competition.

By spring of the following year Pelé was a regular starter with the Santos. And after only two months of play he became so well known around the big leagues that he was chosen to be on Brazil's national team. He was still only sixteen years old.

In his first game for the national team Pelé went in during the second half. He scored the only goal for Brazil as they lost to Argentina, 2 to 1. But just a few days later they played Argentina again. Pelé was a starter and scored another goal. This time Brazil won, 2 to 0.

The next year, 1958, was a World Cup year. Every four years the major soccer-playing countries hold a series of games ending in a finals to decide the victor. The World Cup is given to the best national team in the world.

Pelé was only seventeen years old, but he was chosen for Brazil's World Cup team. In the quarter-finals against Wales, Pelé scored what he feels is one of the most important goals of his career. Brazil won, 1 to 0, and went into the semi-finals, beating France as Pelé scored three times. And in the finals, Pelé scored twice more as Brazil beat Sweden, 5 to 2.

It was Brazil's first World Cup title. Pelé had scored six goals in the three games he played.

Pelé was famous. His feats in the World Cup, with the national team, and with the Santos were the talk of the soccer world. Every team wanted him. Every country wanted him. Then the government of Brazil acted. Pelé was declared a national treasure. Brazil had passed a law to stop people from taking national treasures out of the country. The law was meant to

protect works of art and important relics. But this time the law was used to keep a human being in the country.

Brazil won the World Cup again four years later and then again eight years after that. And over this span of years Pelé's team, the Santos, won state and international team titles time after time. Pelé proved that he truly was a national treasure.

Pelé scored 1220 goals, including 95 for the Brazilian national team. That is a fantastic total for soccer, since many games are low-scoring, often decided by one or two goals.

How could you measure Pelé's feats in soccer in terms of other sports? In baseball, it would be like hitting a home run in every game. Or in basketball, like averaging 50 points per game.

Why has Pelé been such an outstanding player? Speed, of course, is one reason. Pelé can run. And he can change direction and speed quickly. That makes it hard to cover him. Other players can't seem to block him out. But his supreme skill is in ball control. Sometimes it almost seems as if the ball were tied to his foot. Other times he seems to have magical control over it. The ball does exactly what he wants it to do.

Most teams try to stop Pelé by putting two or three players to guard him. Of course, when they do that, Pelé's teammates are in a good spot to score. So Pelé's value to his team is much greater than just the goals he scores. He sets up as many goals for his teammates as he scores himself. It's no wonder that Pelé has been acclaimed all over the world as the greatest soccer player who ever lived.

In 1974 Pelé said he would retire. Giant crowds shouted, *"Pelé, Pelé, Pelé,"* and *"Stay, stay, stay."* But Pelé felt it was time to quit. He was thirty-three years old, and he wanted to relax and spend more time with his wife and two young children. But in 1975, with the permission of the Brazilian government, Pelé signed a contract to play for the New York Cosmos soccer team. He couldn't resist trying to beat the last challenge—making soccer a major sport in the United States. Right from his first appearance, crowds

doubled and tripled. Pelé excited more interest and enthusiasm in soccer than there had ever been before.

Three weeks after arriving in New York, Pelé was seen playing soccer with a bunch of boys in Central Park. When Pelé saw the boys playing, he couldn't stay away, just as he couldn't stay away from the games when he was a barefoot kid kicking an old sock stuffed with newspapers.

In 1978 Pelé retired from the Cosmos. But it is doubtful that he will be able to stay away from soccer for very long.

Baucis and Philemon

OLIVIA COOLIDGE

One time the gods Zeus and Hermes came down to earth in human form and traveled through a certain district, asking for food and shelter as they went. For a long time they received nothing but refusals from both rich and poor. At last they came to a little, one-room cottage with a roof made of reeds from the nearby marsh. There dwelled a poor old couple, Baucis and Philemon.

The two had little to offer, since they lived entirely from the produce of their plot of land and a few goats, fowl, and pigs. Nevertheless they were prompt to ask the strangers in and to set their best before them. The couch that they pulled forward for their guests was roughly put together from willow boughs, and the cushions on it were stuffed with straw. One table leg had to be propped up with a piece of broken pot. But Baucis scrubbed the top of the table with fragrant mint and set some water on the fire. Meanwhile Philemon went out into the garden to fetch a cabbage. Then he lifted down a piece of home-cured bacon from the blackened beam where it hung. While these were cooking, Baucis set her best delicacies on the table. There were ripe olives, sour cherries, fresh onions and radishes, cream cheese, and eggs baked in the ashes of the fire. There was a big earthenware bowl in the middle of the table in which to mix their homemade wine with water.

The second course was fruit. There were nuts, figs, dried dates, plums, grapes, and apples, for this was their best season of the year. Philemon had even had it in mind to kill

their only goose for dinner, and there was a great squawking
and cackling that went on for a long time. Poor old Philemon
wore himself out trying to catch that goose, but somehow
the animal always got away from him until the guests told
him to let it be, for they were well served as it was. It was a
good meal, and the old couple kept urging their guests to eat
and drink, even though they were now consuming in one
day as much food as would ordinarily last the couple a week.

At last the wine sank low in the mixing bowl, and
Philemon rose to fetch some more. But to his astonishment
as he lifted the wineskin to pour, he found the bowl was full
again as though it had not been touched at all. Then he knew
the two strangers must be gods, and he and Baucis were
awed and afraid. But the gods smiled kindly at them, and the
younger, who seemed to do most of the talking, said,
"Philemon, you have welcomed us beneath your roof this
day when richer men refused us shelter. Be sure those shall
be punished who would not help the wandering stranger,
but you shall have whatever reward you choose. Tell us
what you will have."

335

The old man thought for a little with his eyes bent on the ground, and then he said, "We have lived together here for many years, happy even though the times have been hard. But never yet did we see fit to turn a stranger from our gate or to seek a reward for entertaining him. To have spoken with the immortals face to face is a thing few people can boast of. In this small cottage, humble though it is, the gods have sat to eat. It is as unworthy of the honor as we are. If, therefore, you wish to do something for us, turn this cottage into a temple where the gods may always be served and where we may live out the remainder of our days in worship of them."

"You have spoken well," said Hermes, "and you shall have your wish. Yet is there not anything that you would desire for yourselves?"

Philemon thought again at this, stroking his straggly beard. He glanced over at old Baucis with her thin, grey hair and her rough hands as she served at the table, her feet bare on the floor of trodden earth. "We have lived together for many years," he said again, "and in all that time there has never been a word of anger between us. Now, at last, we are growing old and our long companionship is coming to an end. It is the only thing that has helped us in the bad times and has been the source of our joy in the good times. Grant us this one request, that when we come to die, we may perish in the same hour and neither of us be left without the other."

He looked at Baucis and she nodded in approval, so the old couple turned their eyes to the gods.

"It shall be as you desire," said Hermes. "Few people would have made such a good and moderate request."

Thereafter the house became a temple, and the neighbors, amazed at the change, came often to worship and left offerings for the support of the aged priest and priestess there. For many years Baucis and Philemon lived in peace, passing to extreme old age. At last they were so old and bowed that it seemed they could only walk at all if they clutched one another. But still every evening they would shuffle a little way down the path that they might turn and look together at the beautiful little temple and praise the gods for the honor they had bestowed on them. One evening it took them longer than ever to reach the usual spot, and there they turned arm in arm to look back, thinking perhaps that it was the last time their limbs would support them so far. There as they stood, each one felt the other stiffen and change and there was hardly time to turn and say once, "Farewell," before they disappeared. In their place stood two tall trees growing closely side by side with branches interlaced. They seemed to nod and whisper to each other in the passing breeze.

337

Shoeshine Girl

CLYDE ROBERT BULLA

Sarah Ida is angry about spending the summer at Aunt Claudia's.
She has been sent away because her mother is ill, and her parents
can't cope with her willful behavior. Sarah Ida's idea of
independence is having money in her pocket, and when Aunt
Claudia says no allowance, she is determined to get even and find a
job. The shoeshine stand is the only place that will hire a
ten-year-old girl, so Sarah Ida takes the job, believing that her aunt
will give her money rather than let her shine shoes on a street
corner.

Aunt Claudia was waiting on the porch. "Sit down,"
she said, when Sarah Ida came up the steps. "I want to
talk to you." Sarah Ida sat in the porch swing.

"You must never do this again," said Aunt Claudia.
"You must always let me know where you're going. Do
you understand?"

"Yes," said Sarah Ida.

"Where have you been?"

"On the avenue."

"What were you doing?"

"Looking for a job. And I found one."

"You found one?"

"Yes, I did."

"Where?"

"On Grand Avenue. Working for the shoeshine man."

"Who?"

"Al Winkler, the shoeshine man."

Aunt Claudia looked dazed. "How did you know
him?"

"I didn't know him. He had a Help Wanted sign, and I stopped."

"Al Winkler," said Aunt Claudia, as if she were talking to herself. "I remember him so well. He came to the library when I worked there. He hadn't gone to school much, and he wanted to learn more. I helped him choose books." She asked, "Does he want you to work at his stand?"

"He said to talk to you about it."

"Do you want to work for him?" asked Aunt Claudia.

"I told you, I want some money of my own."

"This might be a good way to earn some," said Aunt Claudia.

"You *want* me to shine shoes on Grand Avenue?"

"If that's what you want to do."

Sarah Ida was quiet for a while. Things weren't working out the way she'd planned. She'd never thought Aunt Claudia would let her work in the shoeshine stand, and now Aunt Claudia didn't seem to care!

Unless—Sarah Ida had another thought. Maybe Aunt Claudia didn't believe she'd go through with it. Maybe she was thinking, "That child is playing a game."

Sarah Ida said, "You really want me to go tell Al Winkler I'll work for him?"

"If it's what you want to do," Aunt Claudia said again.

Sarah Ida started down the steps. Aunt Claudia didn't call her back. There was nothing for her to do but go.

She found Al sitting in one of his chairs.

"What did she say?" he asked.

"She said yes."

"You want to start now?"

"I don't care," she said.

He opened a drawer under the platform and took out an old piece of cloth. "Use this for an apron. Tie it around you." She tied it around her waist.

A man stopped at the stand. He was a big man with a round face and a black beard. He climbed into a chair and put his feet on the shoe rests.

"How are you, Mr. Naylor?" said Al.

"Not bad," said the man. "Who's the young lady?"

"She's helping me," said Al. "She needs practice. You mind if she practices on you?"

"I don't mind," said Mr. Naylor.

Al said to Sarah Ida, "I'm going to shine one shoe. You watch what I do. Then you shine the other one."

He took two soft brushes and brushed the man's shoe. "That takes off the dust," he said. "Always start with a clean shoe."

He picked up a jar of water with an old toothbrush in it. With the toothbrush he sprinkled a few drips of water on the shoe. "That makes a better shine."

He opened a round can of brown polish. With his fingers he spread polish on the shoe. "Now you lay your cloth over the shoe," he said. "Stretch it tight—like this. Pull it back and forth—like this. Rub it hard and fast. First the toe—then the sides—then the back."

When he put down the cloth, the shoe shone like glass. He untied the man's shoelace. He drew it a little tighter and tied it again.

He asked Sarah Ida, "Did you see everything I did?"

"Yes," she said.

"All right. Let's see you do it."

She picked up the brushes. She dropped one. When she bent to pick it up, she dropped the other one. Her face grew hot. She brushed the shoe. She sprinkled the water.

"Not so much," Al told her. "You don't need much."

She looked at the brown polish. "Do I have to get this on my fingers?"

"You can put it on with a rag, but it's not the best way. You can rub it in better with your fingers."

"I don't want to get it on my hands."

"Your hands will wash."

She put the polish on with her fingers. She shined Mr. Naylor's shoe. She untied his shoelace, pulled it tight, and tried to tie it again.

Al tied it for her. "It's hard to tie someone else's shoe when you never did it before."

Mr. Naylor looked at his shoes. "Best shine I've had all year," he said. He paid Al. He gave Sarah Ida a dollar bill.

After he had gone, she asked Al, "Why did he give me this?"

"That's your tip," said Al. "You didn't earn it. He gave it to you because you're just getting started."

"Will everybody give me a dollar?" she asked.

"No," he said, "and don't be looking for it."

Others stopped at the stand. Sometimes two or three were there at once. Part of the time Sarah Ida put polish on shoes. Part of the time she used the polishing cloth.

Toward the end of the day she grew tired. Finally Al said, "You can go now." He gave her a dollar. "This is to go with your other dollar."

"Is that all the pay I get?"

"You'll get more when you're worth more," he said. "You can come back tomorrow."

She didn't answer. She turned her back on him and walked away.

But the next morning she went back to the Shoeshine Corner. It wasn't that she liked shining shoes, but things happened at the shoeshine stand. Every customer was different. Every day she found out something new.

Some things she learned by herself such as how much polish to use on a shoe. A thin coat gave a better and quicker shine. Some things Al told her. "When a customer comes here, he gets more than a shine," he said. "He gets to rest in a chair. When you rub with the cloth, it feels good on his feet. When you tie his shoelaces a little tighter, it makes his shoes fit better. My customers go away feeling a little better. Anyway, I hope they do."

One warm cloudy afternoon, he said, "We might as well close up."

"Why?" she asked. "It's only three o'clock."

"It's going to rain. Nobody gets a shine on a rainy day." He began to put away the brushes and shoe polish. She helped him.

"Maybe you can run home before the rain," he said. A few big drops splashed on the sidewalk. "No. Too late now."

They sat under the little roof, out of the rain. "Hear that sound?" he said. "Every time I hear rain on a tin roof, I get to thinking about when I was a boy. We lived in an old truck with a tin roof over the back."

"You lived in a truck?"

"Most of the time. We slept under the tin roof, and when it rained, the sound put me to sleep. We went all over the South in that truck."

"You and your mother and father?"

"My dad and I."

"What were you doing, driving all over the South?"

"My dad sold medicine."

"What kind?"

"Something to make you strong and keep you from getting sick."

"Did you take it?"

"No. I guess it wasn't any good."

She had never heard him talk much about himself before. She wanted him to go on. "Was it fun living in a truck?"

"Fun? I wouldn't say so. Riding along was all right. Sometimes my dad and I stopped close to the woods, and that was all right too. But I never liked it when we were in town selling medicine. Dad would play the mouth harp, and he made me sing. He wanted me to dance a jig, too, but I never could."

343

She tried to imagine Al as a little boy. She couldn't at all. "Why did he want you to sing and dance?" she asked.

"To draw a crowd. When there was a crowd, he sold medicine. We didn't stay anywhere very long. Except once, we stayed in one place six months. My dad did farm work, and I went to school."

He told her about the school. It was just outside a town. The teacher was Miss Miller. The schoolhouse had only one room.

"There was this big stove," he said, "and that winter I kept the fire going. Miss Miller never had to carry coal when I was there."

"Did you like her?" asked Sarah Ida. "Was she a good teacher?"

"Best teacher I ever had. Of course, she was just about the only one. I hadn't been to school much, but she took time to show me things. Do teachers still give medals in school?"

"Sometimes. Not very often."

"Miss Miller gave medals. They were all alike. Every one had a star on it. At the end of school you got one if you were the best in reading or spelling or writing or whatever it was. Everybody wanted a medal, but I knew I'd never get one because I wasn't the best in anything. And at the end of school, you know what happened?"

"What?"

"She called my name. The others all thought it was a joke. But she wasn't laughing. She said, 'Al wins a medal for building the best fires.'"

344

"And it wasn't a joke?" asked Sarah Ida.

"No. She gave me the medal. One of the big boys said, 'You better keep that, Al, because it's the only one you'll ever get.' "

"And did you keep it?"

He held up his watch chain. Something was hanging from it—something that looked like a worn, old coin.

"That's what you won?" asked Sarah Ida. He nodded.

345

"That's a medal?" she said. "That little old piece of tin?"

She shouldn't have said it. As soon as the words were out, she was sorry. Al sat very still. He looked into the street. A moment before, he had been a friend. Now he was a stranger.

He said, "Rain's stopped. For a while, anyway." He slid out of his chair.

She got up, too. "I—" she began. He dragged the folding doors together and locked up.

"Go on. Run," he said. "Maybe you can get home before the rain starts again."

She stood there. "I didn't mean what you think I did," she said. "That medal—it doesn't matter if it's tin or silver or gold. It doesn't matter what it's made of, if it's something you like. I said the wrong thing, but it wasn't what I meant. I—" He had his back to her. She didn't think he was listening. She said, "Listen to me!"

He turned around. "You like ice cream?"

"Yes," she said.

"Come on. I'll buy you a cone."

She went with him, around the corner to Pearl's Ice Cream Shack.

"What kind?" he asked.

"Chocolate," she said.

They sat on a bench inside the Shack and ate their chocolate cones.

"It's raining again," he said.

"Yes," she said.

Then they were quiet, while they listened to the rain.

My Fingers

My fingers are antennae.
Whatever they touch:
Bud, rose, apple,
Cellophane, crutch—
They race the feel
Into my brain,
Plant it there and
Begin again.
This is how I knew
Hot from cold
Before I was even
Two years old.
This is how I can tell,
Though years away,
That elephant hide
Feels leathery grey.
My brain never loses
A touch I bring:
Frail of an eggshell,
Pull of a string,
Beat of a pulse
That tells me life
Thumps in a person
But not in a knife.
Signs that say:
"Please do not touch,"
Disappoint me
Very much.

— Mary O'Neill

What Is Music?

JEAN SELIGMANN and JULIET DANZIGER

What is music? It is not a mystery, as some people seem to suppose. Like almost everything else in the world, music is made up of definite ingredients. The only truly mysterious thing about it is that some human beings have been given the genius to put these different ingredients together in such a way as to create great and beautiful and lasting music.

The best way to understand and appreciate music is to listen to a great deal of it, to play some instrument yourself, and to know something about the various ways works of music are constructed.

Since music is something that we hear, the materials of which music is made are also those that we hear. In other words, music is made up of patterns of sounds arranged in patterns of time.

Sound is an exceedingly important part of our daily lives. Close your eyes for a moment and just listen. Perhaps you hear the rumbling of a train, or someone whistling, a baby crying, a dog barking, the toot of an automobile horn, the wind blowing through the trees, crickets chirping. Or you may hear your neighbor's radio or television set, or perhaps someone playing on the piano or violin. You probably hear something, at any rate, and what you hear is sound, or a number of sounds.

Since music is made up of sounds, let us find out what sound really is. We can see a painting with our eyes and

touch it with our fingers, but sound is something that can only be heard. It is something that comes to our ears through the air.

We live in air. Every time we make the slightest motion we stir the air around us, though we cannot see it move. When you knock on a door or strike a table, a quivering is set up in the wood itself as well as in the air around it. These quiverings, or back-and-forth movements in an object or in the air, are called vibrations. Vibrations travel out into the air, somewhat like the ripples circling out in all directions in a quiet pool of water when you throw a pebble into it.

When vibrations strike our ears, we hear a sound. But we would never have heard a sound if something had not started the vibration, if there had not been the air to carry the vibration to us, and if we had no ears to receive it.

There are many kinds of sounds. They can be loud, soft, sweet, harsh, dull, sharp, shrill, and so on. Usually, sounds that are harsh or unpleasant, or in some other way distressing to our ears, are called noise. When sounds are agreeable to the ear we call them musical sounds, or tones. Actually, it is often hard to distinguish between noise

349

and music. And often, too, it is a matter of opinion. When you blow across the top of a bottle, for instance, is the sound a noise or a musical tone? Perhaps to someone who is trying to read the newspaper it is a noise, but to you it may sound like the low tone of a flute. At a symphony concert the crash of cymbals is musical when it comes in at the right place, but most people would consider it a noise if the cymbals fell to the floor during the concert.

What is a musical tone? Almost all things that we can see or touch can be more or less easily described. Bricks have roughness, shape, and color. Beads have smoothness, roundness, and color. Flowers have smell, form, and color. But we cannot see or touch musical tones. They can be described only by how they sound to us. And in order to give a description of a musical tone, we shall have to describe it in four different ways.

We say that a tone is high or low. The highness or lowness of a tone is known as its pitch. The tone of a police whistle has a high pitch. The average human voice used in everyday speech is of medium pitch. The rumble of thunder is of low pitch. You can make an interesting experiment in pitch yourself. Take a tall glass. Strike the side of it with a spoon. Then pour water slowly into the glass, hitting it with the spoon as it fills up. You will hear the pitch of the tone go higher and higher. Pitch depends on the number of vibrations per second of the sounding body that produces it. Our ears can hear pitches ranging from about 16 to 16,000 vibrations per second.

Besides having pitch, a tone also has duration—that is, longness or shortness. If you ring a doorbell and keep your finger on the button for a long time, you are producing a long tone. If you lift your finger immediately after pressing the button, you will produce a short tone.

A musical tone also has loudness or softness, or intensity. If you strike a key on the piano very lightly, it will produce a very soft tone. If you strike it hard, it will produce a loud tone.

Tones also have what is known as tone color. We know that objects like bricks and beads and flowers have color. But tone color is not green or red or blue, naturally, for a tone is not something we can see. Tone color is rather the quality of a tone. A tone played on the violin, for example, has a different tone color from a tone of the same pitch played on the piano or the saxophone. Each musical instrument has its own tone color. No two singers have voices that sound exactly alike. Every individual human voice has its own distinctive tone color. We can speak of tone colors as thick, thin, light, dark, sharp, brilliant, dull, smooth, coarse, warm, cold, fuzzy, velvety, round, or even neutral.

Pitch, duration, intensity, and tone color—every musical tone has these four characteristics. No one is more important than any other. In listening to music, however, we do not separate these characteristics one from the others. They are all blended together.

Musical tones, then, are the raw materials of music. Just as a wall may be built up of bricks, or a necklace made up of beads, or a bouquet made up of flowers, or words made up of letters, so music is made up of musical tones. But we must put the bricks in rows and pile them up to make a wall; the beads must be strung to form a necklace; the flowers must be arranged to make a bouquet, the letters put together to form a word. Musical tones, too, must be arranged in some order to create music.

January

From *ALICE YAZZIE'S YEAR*

The snow slowed the world,
the Navajo world.
"Go see if the sheep are fine,"
Grandfather Tsosie tells Alice Yazzie.
"The hay is frozen
and so is the ground," says Alice, returning.
"The horses look like they blame me
for causing this cold."

Her nose red, her chin buried in sheepskin,
she carries the smallest lamb
into the hogan.
"Just for the night," says Alice Yazzie
holding the lamb.
"He's all new and starry.
He's too new to be cold."
Grandfather grunts.
He doesn't say no.

352

Alice heats milk in a bottle
over burning pinyon.
Grandfather watches.
The new lamb sucks.
The pinyon burns low.
The lamb goes to sleep.
His nose is a black star.

"It *is* cold out there," Alice tells Grandfather
as she goes to bed.
Grandfather nods.
He wears a red flannel shirt Alice gave him for Christmas.
He looks at the low fire.
He looks at the lamb.
Grandfather says
to Alice Yazzie,
to Alice Ben Yazzie,
"It was almost this cold
the night you were born."

—Ramona Maher

New Friends and Old

JULIA CUNNINGHAM

Maybe is a young mole who prefers the excitement of the upper
world to living with the other moles underground. He has become a
good friend of the fox and is sharing the fox's den.

The morning was deep into autumn. The trees were
flaring high in their scarlet and gold leaves, and the
frosted air was pungent with the sweetness of mold. Just
to breathe made Maybe laugh as he stepped from the den
to sun himself.

"Feeling it, are you?" asked the fox, just behind him.

"Feeling what?" asked the mole, knowing exactly
what his friend meant but wanting a word for it.

"The joy."

Maybe nodded, smiling.

"Want to pay a visit to an old friend?" said the fox
casually, but the mole heard the importance of the
question. "It will mean a long hike, but I will be your
horse."

The mole saw that the fox had strapped a bag of
provisions onto his back. "Gladly," said Maybe. "But
where are we going?"

"To pass an hour or two with an old enemy of mine,
the great hunting hound."

Maybe looked his surprise.

The fox laughed. "Yes, we shared so many hunts
together, he chasing, me fleeing, neither ever winning,
that finally when he retired from his job as leader of the
hounds, we just naturally became friends."

The mole, who had learned never to question the fox's eccentricities, for they always turned out to be some part of wisdom, climbed up to his place behind the fox's shoulders and called out, "Let's go!"

So the fox went at an easy trot through the entire morning of fields and streams and brilliant woods. At last he arrived at a white fence so long the mole could see no end to it.

"Here we are," said the fox, and the mole slid down to the ground, content to stretch and roll for a moment in the clipped grass.

The fox barked three times, then again, and there from behind the fence appeared the noble shape of a hound who, in spite of aging jowls and a slightly grayed hide, would have been acknowledged an aristocrat in any royal pack.

The two animals bowed to each other, then relaxed into a kind of simple frolic, pretending affectionate blows with their paws. Next the fox introduced his two friends, and they all three sat down and began to catch up on the events of their separate worlds.

355

"Retirement really isn't too boring," said the hound in response to the fox's interest. "I'm particularly pleased not to be forced to corner any more foxes." He smiled widely.

"You were always more than fair," commented the fox. "In fact several times you gave me the advantage."

"Did I now?" said the hound. "Perhaps. But such things never got back to the Master of the Hunt. I saw to it. Had tight control over the others."

"What was behind your kindness?" asked the fox. "You were certainly not trained in that direction."

The massive dog looked into the fox's eyes. "Respect," he replied.

The fox's tail switched with pleasure. "Let's have a run, shall we?" he said to cover his embarrassment. "Show the mole how we did it?"

Maybe climbed back into his place as rider. "Hang on tight!" instructed the fox, and he loped swiftly into the nearest cover of trees.

The hound did not move.

"He'll give me a good head start," explained the fox, increasing his pace until, soon, even the fences were out of sight.

But a few minutes later the mole wondered why the fox halted and glanced back, his eyes puzzled. Then the fox worked his way out of the trees and climbed a hill. But nowhere in the now visible distance was a glimpse of the hound. Instead there came the far-off sound of a horn.

The fox quivered. "The hunt!" he exclaimed, shock in his voice. "They're off and away!"

Now like an accompaniment to the hunting horn they could hear the hounds baying.

"Let's go home," murmured the mole. But the fox remained motionless, listening with an alertness the mole had never witnessed before in his friend. It was as if his ears and mind were sorting out all the smallest movements of the countryside.

"They're heading toward us," he said to the mole. "I must run. I will leave you in a safe place, and if I can, come back for you. If not you must return by yourself. Do not wait beyond dusk."

"No," said Maybe. "I will stay with you, no matter what." He clenched his paws more firmly in the fox's ruff and did not speak again. The fox was within a concentration so intense he seemed to have forgotten the mole. He had to.

The noise of the hounds was nearer now. With a high bound the fox dived back into the shelter of the woods. He began to run in a zig-zag pattern. Once he splashed a hundred yards through a stream and paused to rest on the far bank. His breathing was shorter and Maybe could feel his muscles quiver.

Perhaps he delayed a little too long. Perhaps he was out of practice. For, like a tangle of thunder, the pack broke through the trees downstream and stopped, sniffling and snuffling, trying to recapture the scent. And at that instant Maybe saw the great hound bringing up the rear. He was lunging ferociously at the rear legs of the other dogs, biting where he could, ignoring the snarling attacks of the younger hounds. Maybe realized he was trying to stop the hunt. The old dog's chest was bleeding from the resistance of the others.

Then as if to get rid of this fierce interference, the lead hound signaled a mass charge and each hound

wheeled about-face, formed a tight circle and stood
against their former leader, teeth bared, their throats
heavy with growling.

The fox said one word, "Good-bye," and barked so
sharply the mole's ears rang.

As if reversed by a giant wind, the hounds turned and
in one wave poured toward the fox, leaving the hound
alone and unable to save his friend.

Suddenly the mole felt as though he were in the eye
of a cyclone, so fast did the fox skim the ground. He later
had a vague remembrance of being carried through an
orchard, of ducking through the doors of a vast barn and
out again, scattering chickens and pigs like dust, and of
another wild circling through trees and thickets that tore
little scratches in his skin. He sensed, his eyes shut, his
paws just barely holding on, the terrible ordeal of the fox
and he could feel the pounding of his heart all the way
up through his backbone. But all the mole could do was
to become all one small force of love and faith for his
friend, to have a kind of senseless trust that his love and
faith would get to the fox and somehow help.

Abruptly the terror of the hounds vanished, the flight halted, and the mole smelled the sweetness of the den all around him. He tumbled off the fox's back. The fox lay flat and barely breathing on the warm, earthen floor. Quickly the mole brought him water on a leaf and put it under his nose. The fox lapped awkwardly at the cooling liquid, but his eyes opened.

The mole couldn't seem to stop patting the fox's head as if he might suddenly become unreal and not be there at all.

The fox tried to smile but he was too exhausted. But he could whisper. "Maybe," he said very low, "we're home."

"And you saved not just me and you," said the mole, "but the hound as well."

"I had to," said the fox. "They would have killed him and besides—" His voice drifted into silence.

"Besides what?" prompted the mole gently. "Why?"

The fox raised his head and there reappeared in his eyes a kind of light that reminded Maybe of the morning star.

"Respect," said the fox and lay back to welcome sleep.

Lilliann Der

CAROL ANN BALES

One time last summer some kids started asking me: "Are you from China or Japan?" It's pretty hard to explain. I told them I'm not from China or Japan. I was born in Chicago. But I am a Chinese-American.

I used to be very shy. I didn't know how to answer questions like that. But after kindergarten I started to talk a lot. I'm in the fifth grade this year. I don't talk so much any more, but I'm not exactly shy—just sometimes.

My name is Lilliann Der. My American name, that is. My Chinese name is Der Wai Lee. Everyone at home calls me *Lee Lee*, which sounds like Lily. Lee means a "little jasmine flower" in Chinese.

My father is assistant manager of the Hong Kong Noodle Company in Chinatown, and we live in Wilmette, a suburb of Chicago.

My parents and my grandmother were born in China in a place called Toishan. My grandfather's family lived in China, but I think he was born in the United States. He and some other Chinese men founded the Hong Kong Noodle Company.

When he retired, he went back to China to live. He bought a big house and some land. But when the communist government came to power they didn't allow people to own land, so my grandfather moved his family to Hong Kong and then to the United States. My mother's family did the same thing. I wasn't born yet, but that's what my mother told me.

My grandfather is buried in a cemetery in Chicago, in a special Chinese part. We visit there on Ching Ming—that's Chinese Memorial Day—and on the date that he died, and on a couple of other days. We clean off his grave, put flowers on it, and take pictures.

Grandma lives with us. She grows Chinese vegetables in our back yard. When she gets up in the morning, she reads the Bible for an hour or two in her room, and then she goes outside. Some days she stays out all day.

She planted seventeen or eighteen different kinds of vegetables last summer. Chinese broccoli, *bok choy*—that's Chinese cabbage—mustard greens, string beans, peppers, tomatoes, and three kinds of melons. And some other vegetables that I can't remember.

The summer before last, she grew a big Chinese winter melon. It weighed thirty pounds. Everybody said it was the biggest one they'd ever seen. Grandma likes to make melon soup in the winter. She cut the big one up into pieces to give to our friends.

We used to have more flowers when we first moved to Wilmette, but Grandma keeps trimming them back. Grandma used to grow a lot more vegetables in China. She raised geese and chickens in China, too. She lived in a farm village. I think she misses it. Grandma says she'd like to go back to that village in China for a visit—but just for a visit. She wouldn't stay.

We ask Grandma's opinion before we do anything that's important, and I always say good morning and good night to her. That's how I show that I love and respect her.

Grandma always tells us to be honest at home and away from home, obedient to our parents, and kind to others.

Summer is my favorite time of year because we go places. We take swimming lessons, and sometimes we go apple picking, and sometimes we visit our friends or relatives. Like Grandma Leu. Grandma Leu lives in Chinatown.

She's not really my grandmother, but we call her Grandma because it's polite. We're never supposed to call Chinese grownups by their names. If they're our parents' age, we're supposed to call them Auntie or Uncle. If they're our grandmother's age, we call them Grandma or Grandpa. But in Chinese those names are special names—not the same names we use for our real grandparents or aunts and uncles.

Grandma Leu always takes us to see her vegetable garden. I like to stand on her porch. From there all you can see are Chinese vegetable gardens. Grandma Leu always has a nice garden. She takes a knife and cuts vegetables for us to take home. Sometimes we play in the school playground across the street.

I have one very good school friend. She's black. Camille and I met in the second grade, and we've been friends ever since. A few times we broke our friendship, but we made up. It's hard to keep a friendship that long. You find it hard to keep away from an argument. The rest of my friends are white, like Robin, except for my Chinese friends—and some of them are my relatives.

Camille, Robin, and I all belong to Girl Scouts. Robin's mother is a leader. We go to a meeting one night a week.

I don't have many chores during the school year. I have to practice my piano lessons, but I like to do that. Sometimes when Grandma and Mommy are busy, I feed Rosalie. We call her *Moy Moy*, which means "little sister" in Chinese. She's learning to talk. She says words in Chinese unless they're easier to say in English.

Of all the holidays, Christmas is my favorite, and Halloween is my second favorite. I guess I like the Moon Festival—because I like to eat moon cakes—and the Chinese New

Year best of the Chinese holidays.

These are the things that remind me of the Chinese New Year. The house smells like flowers because Grandma always puts narcissus bulbs in bowls of water to bloom for New Year's Day. We each get a new outfit. This year Grandma made Mommy, Caroline, Vivian, and me new pants suits. And we make Chinese pastry.

You have to make pastry because you visit your friends and relatives on the Chinese New Year, or they visit you, and you want to have pastry to give to them. We make egg rolls and pastry called *ham gok*, *tim gok*, and *lor bok go* in Chinese. We always put two tangerines in boxes of pastry for friends. That's for good luck.

In Chinatown there's always a big celebration on the Sunday closest to the Chinese New Year. It's fun. It's also noisy—and crowded. You hear a lot of firecrackers, and I mean a *lot*, and people stand in the streets to watch the lion dance.

Chinese New Year comes about a month after the January 1 New Year's Day because the Chinese calendar is different from the

calendar used in this country.

On January 1 my father goes to pay our dues to the family association—families with the same last name as ours belong to it. Some of the Chinese men buy incense to burn on Chinese New Year's Eve to help them remember their ancestors.

My grandma says we are a year older not just on our birthdays, but on Chinese New Year's Day, too. She says the Chinese New Year is important because it is the time of the year to make plans for the future.

I made three resolutions for this year: to be more patient, to be less shy, and—I forgot the other one.

363

Duke Pishposh of Pash

JAY WILLIAMS

On a day in early spring, Prince William of Orange rode into the city of Delft. He was the leader of the armies of the Netherlands, and he was on his way to Amsterdam to meet with his captains. As he passed through the square on his way to the burgomaster's house, he heard a commotion. A small crowd of people had surrounded a man in a bright red jacket. Some were arguing at the tops of their voices, and some were laughing.

The prince rode to the spot and commanded them to be silent. They recognized him immediately and fell back quietly.

"What is happening here?" he asked.

One man stepped forward. "Your Highness," said he, "I am a cheese merchant. This fellow in the red coat told me he had a perfect way of getting rid of mice. He said the gadget was guaranteed to work every time, and so I bought it for a hundred florins. This is what he gave me. It's a swindle!" He held out a hammer and a block of wood. "He told me to put each mouse on the block of wood and hit it with the hammer."

Prince William could not help laughing. "He was right; it will work every time. But you are right, too; it was a swindle." He looked at the man in the red jacket. "What is your name?" he said.

"Tyl Uilenspiegel, Your Highness," said Tyl with a low bow.

"I have heard of you," said the prince, frowning. "Return this man's money and come with me."

Tyl did not dare to disobey. So he gave the money back and followed the prince to the burgomaster's house.

There Prince William said sternly, "You are a rogue and a trickster. Can you give me one reason why I should not send you to prison?"

"It's not my fault, Your Highness," said Tyl. "It's just that everyone I meet is so foolish. All I have to do is ask, and people give me money. Why, I'll wager I can get the richest man in Delft to give me anything I want."

"I don't believe it," said the prince. "If you can do such a thing, I'll set you free."

"Very well," Tyl said. "All I need is five gold pieces to start with."

The prince gave them to him and said, "I must stay in Delft for two days. That is all the time you have."

"It's enough," said Tyl.

The richest man in Delft was named Lucas Koop. He was suspicious and bad-tempered and stingy. He lived in a fine house and spent one half of his time counting his money, and the other half dreaming of ways to get more. Next door to Lucas Koop's big house was a little house belonging to a poor shoemaker, Jan Brouwer. Jan was hard-working and kind and the biggest gossip in town.

That night a ragged beggar with a patch over one eye knocked at the shoemaker's door. "I have traveled many miles, and I have no money," he said. "Please let me warm myself at your fire for a little while."

"Come in, come in," said the shoemaker. "You must be hungry, too, and you're just in time for supper. We haven't much, but what there is, you're welcome to share."

In came Tyl—for of course it was he. The shoemaker's wife greeted him, and the shoemaker's two children stared at him curiously. He warmed himself before the fire and told them stories of his travels. They listened in wonder, for they had never been away from Delft. Then they all sat down to a simple meal of bread and sausages and beer, and if there wasn't much food, there was plenty of friendliness to season it.

After dinner Tyl said, "I thank you, good people. Now I must be on my way again."

"Nonsense!" said Jan Brouwer. "The night is cold and dark, and I wouldn't think of turning you out. We haven't any spare beds, but you are welcome to sleep before the fire." He filled a bag with straw, placed it near the hearth, and gave Tyl a blanket. Tyl curled up on the straw and slept soundly, for he had spent the night in many worse places.

In the morning they had bread and milk for breakfast, and then Tyl stood up, looking suddenly much taller and more dignified. "I have something to tell you," he said to the shoemaker. "I am no beggar, but Duke Pishposh of Pash. Every spring I travel about in disguise, looking for people who are kind and generous. When I find them, I reward them for each thing they give me. You have given me five things—a roof over my head, a good dinner, a fire, a bed, and breakfast. Here are five gold pieces."

He put the money into the shoemaker's hand. The poor man stared, and his wife and children stared, too, for they had never before seen so much gold all at once.

Then Tyl left them, and all that day the shoemaker could not keep from telling everyone he met about his good fortune. So it wasn't long before the news reached his rich neighbor Lucas Koop.

That night Tyl, still dressed in beggar's rags and wearing a patch over one eye, knocked at the door of Lucas Koop's house. A servant appeared.

"The· night is cold, and my way is hard," said Tyl. "Please may I come in and warm myself?"

The servant bowed. "My master has given orders that any ragged beggar—especially one with a patch over his eye—should be admitted. Come in, and I will take you to him."

Tyl grinned to himself and followed the servant into a paneled room full of splendid furniture and rich paintings. A fire was burning in a big tiled stove, and Lucas Koop was standing before it. When he saw Tyl, he came forward to greet him, trying to smile although he had no practice at it.

"Welcome!" he croaked. "Glad to see you. I'm always kind to beggars. Anyone will tell you that I am the most generous man in the world. I'm sure you must be hungry—"

"That's right," said Tyl.

"Then come this way." And Koop led him into a dining room where, at a long table, a feast was spread.

"What handsome silver dishes these are," said Tyl.

"Do you like them? Please take one as a gift," Koop said.

After he had eaten as much as he could hold, Tyl said, "Now I must be on my way again."

"No, no," said Koop. "You are my guest. I have a bedroom specially prepared for you." He showed Tyl a room in which there was a big four-poster bed, spread with linen sheets and heaped with feather quilts. On a table beside the bed were a bowl of fruit, a pitcher of wine, and a silver goblet.

"What a beautiful goblet," said Tyl.

"Do you like it? Please take it as a gift," said Koop. "Anything in the house is yours. Help yourself." And in his head, he added up the number of gold pieces he would get the next morning from Duke Pishposh of Pash.

But the next morning, his guest was gone. So were the silver dish, the silver goblet, a gold tobacco box, a pewter candlestick, and a great many other expensive things. On the table was a note that said, "Come to the burgomaster's house for your reward. Duke Pishposh of Pash."

Full of joy, Lucas Koop scurried to the burgomaster's house. There he found Prince William of Orange having breakfast with the beggar, who no longer had a patch over his eye and wore a red jacket instead of rags.

"Here is the rich man I was telling you about," said Tyl to the prince as Lucas Koop came in. "He gave me the things in this sack." And he showed Prince William the silver dish, the silver goblet, the tobacco box, the candlestick, and all the rest.

"Is it true?" the prince asked.

"Yes, Your Highness," answered Koop.

"There you are," said Tyl. "And what's more, I didn't even have to ask him for anything. He gave me a splendid dinner and a soft bed and told me to help myself to anything in the house. Isn't that so?"

"Of course," said Lucas Koop. "Now, where is my reward?"

Tyl rose and stretched out his hand. "You already have everything anyone could want," he said solemnly. "Your reward is the comfortable feeling that you have done a good deed."

"What?" shrieked Koop. "Is that all?"

"You have my thanks as well," said Tyl.

Lucas Koop jumped up and down in fury. "I don't want your thanks. You gave five gold pieces to Jan Brouwer. I ought to have five hundred!"

"Jan Brouwer let me in because he thought I was a poor beggar," Tyl replied. "So he deserved the money. But you let me in because you thought I was a rich duke. So you don't deserve a thing."

"I agree," said Prince William. "You are a little too greedy, Master Koop. You may go, and Tyl may keep what you gave him."

Koop saw that the prince was not to be trifled with. He

369

turned and silently went home. Then the prince said to Tyl, "You are free. You have won your bet."

"Thank you, Your Highness," said Tyl, picking up the sackful of treasures. "But to tell the truth, I won my bet two days ago."

"What do you mean?" asked the prince.

"You are richer than Lucas Koop, and so when you arrived, you became the richest man in Delft. Two days ago I asked you for five gold pieces, and you gave them to me without a murmur." He hoisted the sack over his shoulder. "Good-bye, Your Highness," he said with a smile. "You see, it's just as I said. It's not my fault—I only ask, and people give me whatever I want."

The Swallow and the Other Birds

AESOP

Once a farmer was planting some hemp seeds in a field where a swallow and some other birds were hopping around, picking up their food.

"Watch out for that man," said the swallow to the other birds.

"Why, what is he doing?" said the others.

"That is hemp seed he is planting," explained the swallow. "You must pick up every one of the seeds, or else you will be sorry later." But the other birds didn't pay any attention to the swallow's words.

By and by the hemp grew up and was made into cord. Nets were made from the cord. And many of the birds that had not taken the swallow's advice were caught in those nets, made of that very hemp that grew from the seeds they had not bothered to eat.

"What did I tell you?" said the swallow. "But you wouldn't listen, so now you must suffer."

Destroy the seed of evil
or it will grow up to destroy you.

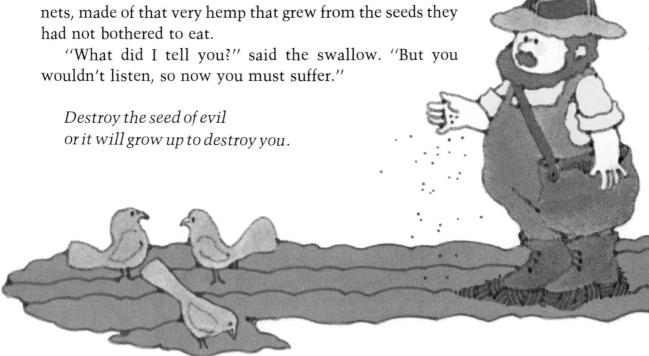

The Queen's Croquet Ground

LEWIS CARROLL

Alice, who is about your age, has fallen down a deep rabbit hole into a strange underground world. She has already spoken with a caterpillar, met a disappearing cat, and attended an unusual tea party. In this chapter from *Alice's Adventures in Wonderland*, Alice meets the Queen of Hearts and becomes involved in a very challenging game of croquet.

A large rosetree stood near the entrance of the garden. The roses growing on it were white, but there were three gardeners at it, busily painting them red. Alice thought this a very curious thing, and she went nearer to watch them. Just as she came up to them she heard one of them say, "Look out now, Five! Don't go splashing paint over me like that!"

"I couldn't help it," said Five, in a sulky tone. "Seven jogged my elbow."

"That's right, Five!" said Seven. "Always lay the blame on others!"

"*You'd* better not talk!" said Five. "I heard the Queen say yesterday you deserved to be beheaded!"

"What for?" said the one who had spoken first.

"That's none of your business, Two!" said Seven.

"Yes, it is his business!" said Five, "and I'll tell him—it was for bringing the cook tuliproots instead of onions."

Seven flung down his brush and had just begun, "Well, of all the unjust things—" when his eye chanced to fall upon Alice, as she stood watching them. He checked himself suddenly. The others looked around also, and all of them bowed low.

"Would you tell me, please," said Alice, a little timidly, "why you are painting those roses?"

Five and Seven said nothing, but looked at Two. Two began, in a low voice, "Why, the fact is, Miss, this ought to have been a red rosetree, but we put a white one in by mistake, and if the Queen was to find it out, we should all have our heads cut off, you know. So you see, Miss, we're doing our best, afore she comes, to—" At this moment Five, who had been anxiously looking across the garden, called out "The Queen! The Queen!" and the three gardeners instantly threw themselves flat upon their faces. There was a sound of many footsteps. Alice looked around, eager to see the Queen.

First came ten soldiers carrying clubs. These soldiers were all shaped like the three gardeners, oblong and flat, with their hands and feet at the corners. Next came ten courtiers. These were ornamented all over with diamonds and walked two and two, as the soldiers did. After these came the royal children. There were ten of them, and the little dears came jumping merrily along hand in hand,

in couples. They were all ornamented with hearts. Next came the guests, mostly Kings and Queens. Then followed the Knave of Hearts, carrying the King's crown on a crimson velvet cushion. And, last of all this grand procession, came the King and Queen of Hearts.

Alice was rather doubtful whether she ought not to lie down on her face like the three gardeners, but she could not remember ever having heard of such a rule at processions. And besides, what would be the use of a procession, she thought, if people had all to lie down on their faces so that they couldn't see it? So she stood where she was and waited.

When the procession came opposite Alice, they all stopped and looked at her. The Queen said severely, "Who is this?" She said it to the Knave of Hearts, who only bowed and smiled in reply.

"Idiot!" said the Queen, tossing her head impatiently. Turning to Alice, she went on, "What's your name, child?"

"My name is Alice, so please your Majesty," said Alice very politely. But she added, to herself, "Why, they're only a pack of cards, after all. I needn't be afraid of them!"

"And who are *these*?" said the Queen, pointing to the three gardeners who were lying around the rosetree. You see, as they were lying on their faces, and the pattern on their backs was the same as the rest of the pack, she could not tell whether they were gardeners or soldiers, or courtiers, or three of her own children.

"How should *I* know?" said Alice, surprised at her own courage. "It's no business of *mine*."

The Queen turned crimson with fury, and after glaring at her for a moment like a wild beast, began screaming, "Off with her head! Off—"

"Nonsense!" said Alice, very loudly and decidedly, and the Queen was silent.

The King laid his hand upon her arm, and timidly said, "Consider, my dear. She is only a child!"

The Queen turned angrily away from him, and said to the Knave, "Turn them over!"

The Knave did so, very carefully, with one foot.

"Get up!" said the Queen in a shrill, loud voice, and the three gardeners instantly jumped up and began bowing to the King, the Queen, the royal children, and everybody else.

"Stop that!" screamed the Queen. "You make me dizzy." And then, turning to the rosetree, she went on, "What have you been doing here?"

"May it please your Majesty," said Two, in a very humble tone, going down on one knee as he spoke, "we were trying—"

"I see!" said the Queen, who had meanwhile been examining the roses. "Off with their heads!" and the procession moved on, three of the soldiers remaining behind to execute the unfortunate gardeners, who ran to Alice for protection.

"You won't be beheaded!" said Alice, and she put them into a large flowerpot that stood near. The three soldiers wandered about for a minute or two, looking for them, and then quietly marched off after the others.

"Are their heads off?" shouted the Queen.

"Their heads are gone, if it please your Majesty!" the soldiers shouted in reply.

"Can you play croquet?" shouted the Queen.

The soldiers were silent and looked at Alice, as the question was evidently meant for her.

375

"Yes!" shouted Alice.

"Come on then!" roared the Queen, and Alice joined the procession, wondering what would happen next.

"Get to your places!" shouted the Queen in a voice of thunder, and people began running about in all directions, tumbling up against each other. However, they got settled down in a minute or two, and the game began.

Alice thought she had never seen such a curious croquet ground in her life. It was all ridges and furrows; the croquet balls were live hedgehogs and the mallets live flamingoes; and the soldiers had to double themselves up and stand on their hands and feet to make the arches.

The chief difficulty Alice found at first was in managing her flamingo. She succeeded in getting its body tucked away, comfortably enough under her arm, with its legs hanging down. But just as she had got its neck nicely straightened out and was going to give the hedgehog a blow with its head, it would twist itself around and look up into her face, with such a puzzled expression that she could not help bursting out laughing. And when she had got its head down and was going to begin again, it was very provoking to find that the hedgehog had unrolled itself and was in the act of crawling away. Besides all this, there was generally a ridge or a furrow in the way wherever she wanted to send the hedgehog. And as the doubled-up soldiers were always getting up and walking off to other parts of the ground, Alice soon came to the conclusion that it was a very difficult game indeed.

The players all played at once without waiting for turns, quarreling all the while and fighting for the hedgehogs. In a very short time the Queen was in a furious passion and went stamping about, shouting, "Off with his head!" or "Off with her head!"

Alice began to feel very uneasy. To be sure, she had not as yet had any dispute with the Queen, but she knew that it might happen any minute. And then, she thought, what would become of me? They're dreadfully fond of beheading people here. The great wonder is that there's anyone left alive!

She was looking about for some way of escape, wondering whether she could get away without being seen, when she noticed a curious appearance in the air. It puzzled her very much at first, but after watching it a minute or two she made it out to be a grin. And she said to herself, "It's the Cheshire Cat. Now I shall have somebody to talk to."

"How are you getting along?" said the Cat, as soon as there was mouth enough for it to speak.

Alice waited till the eyes appeared, and then nodded. It's no use speaking to it, she thought, till its ears have come, or at least one of them. In another minute the whole head appeared, and then Alice put down her flamingo and began an account of the game, feeling very glad she had someone to listen to her. The Cat seemed to think that there was enough of it now in sight, and no more of it appeared.

"I don't think they play at all fairly," Alice began, in rather a complaining tone. "And they all quarrel so dreadfully one can't hear oneself speak. And they don't seem to have any rules in particular; at least, if there are, nobody attends to them. And you've no idea how confusing it is all the things being alive. For instance: there's the arch I've got to go through next, walking about at the other end of the ground. And I should have croqueted the Queen's hedgehog just now, only it ran away when it saw mine coming!"

"How do you like the Queen?" said the Cat in a low voice.

"Not at all," said Alice. "She's so extremely—" Just then she noticed that the Queen was close behind her, listening. So she went on "—likely to win that it's hardly worthwhile finishing the game."

The Queen smiled and passed on.

"Who are you talking to?" said the King, coming up to Alice and looking at the Cat's head with great curiosity.

"It's a friend of mine—a Cheshire Cat," said Alice. "Allow me to introduce it."

"I don't like the look of it at all," said the King. "However, it may kiss my hand if it likes."

"I'd rather not," the Cat remarked.

"Don't be impertinent," said the King, "and don't look at me like that!" He got behind Alice as he spoke.

"A cat may look at a king," said Alice. "I've read that in some book, but I don't remember where."

"Well, it must be removed," said the King very decidedly, and he called to the Queen, who was passing at the moment, "My dear! I wish you would have this cat removed!"

The Queen had only one way of settling all difficulties, great or small. "Off with his head!" she said without even looking around.

"I'll fetch the executioner myself," said the King eagerly, and he hurried off.

Alice thought she might as well go back and see how the game was going, as she heard the Queen's voice in the distance, screaming with passion. She had already heard her sentence three of the players to be executed for having missed their turns. She did not like the look of things at all, as the game was in such confusion that she never knew whether it was her turn or not. So she went off in search of her hedgehog.

The hedgehog was engaged in a fight with another hedgehog, which seemed to Alice an excellent opportunity for croqueting one of them with the other. The only difficulty was that her flamingo had gone to the other side of the garden, where Alice could see it trying in a helpless sort of way to fly up into a tree.

By the time she had caught the flamingo and brought it back, the fight was over, and both the hedgehogs were out of sight. But it doesn't matter much, thought Alice, as all the arches are gone from this side of the ground.

379

So she tucked it away under her arm, that it might not escape again, and went back to have a little more conversation with her friend.

When she got back to the Cheshire Cat, she was surprised to find quite a large crowd collected around it. There was a dispute going on between the executioner, the King, and the Queen, who were all talking at once, while all the rest were quite silent and looked very uncomfortable.

The moment Alice appeared, she was appealed to by all three to settle the question and they repeated their arguments to her. As they all spoke at once, she found it very hard to make out exactly what they said.

The executioner's argument was that you couldn't cut off a head unless there was a body to cut it off from, that he had never had to do such a thing before, and that he wasn't going to begin now.

The King's argument was that anything that had a head could be beheaded and that you weren't to talk nonsense.

The Queen's argument was that if something wasn't done about it in less than no time she'd have everybody executed, all around. It was this last remark that had made the whole party look so grave and anxious.

Alice could think of nothing else to say but "It belongs to the Duchess. You'd better ask her about it."

"She's in prison," the Queen said to the executioner. "Fetch her here." And the executioner went off like an arrow.

The Cat's head began fading away the moment the executioner was gone, and by the time he had come back with the Duchess, it had entirely disappeared. So the King and the executioner ran wildly up and down looking for it, though they never found it. And the rest of the party went back to the game.

Cluster 8

The Dream Runner

AUDREE DISTAD

Sam is a young Indian whose only happiness comes from running. He works after school in a cattle barn. There his co-worker, Old Clete, tells him about the vision quests that Sioux boys had once made in the nearby mountains.

"Maybe if I'd gone on one of them vision quests, like my granddad told me, that would have put me on the right track," Clete said. "Might have found some magic power to help me."

Sam felt a story coming. "What are they?"

"They? Who?"

"Those vision quests . . ."

"Ah, it was what old-time Indians believed. Talk about seeing things that aren't there. . . . They put great stock in visions—to give them power, sort of help them over the rough spots."

"Power?"

"Kind of magic, you might call it. Not muscle power, exactly, but inside power. Backbone, so to speak. They knew it'd be there when they needed it."

"How'd they get the visions? Was it a ceremony?"

"Sort of a test, you could say. Most boys went through it when they were about your age, I guess. How old are you?"

Sam straightened. "Thirteen, pretty near."

"Somewhere around there. When a boy was old enough, the medicine man'd lead him out of camp, off to a hill, high up. And he'd sit the boy down facing north

. . . ." Clete paused. "I think it had to be north. Anyway,
that boy stayed there all alone, with no food or water, for
three days and nights . . ."

"Nothing at all?"

"Not a thing. He was to sit and wait for a vision. Me,
I'd a seen fried eggs and hash browns, but an old-time
Indian boy, you see, he hoped some spirit would show
itself and give him its power so he could act bravely. It
was a kind of initiation from being a boy into being a
man."

"And then what?"

"Ain't that enough?"

"No," said Sam, "you gotta tell me the rest of it.
What'd the spirit look like?"

383

Clete sighed. "I should of never started this story with you. You're worse'n a dog hanging on a bone. You got to remember it's been a long time since I heard this, and my granddad wasn't such a spring chicken when he told it to me either, so between the two of us, we forgot a powerful lot."

"What you remember then."

"Don't rush me. I haven't thought about this for years. Sure appealed to me when I was little. Anyway, that boy sat there on top of the hill, and for him that was the center of the world. What he saw around him was the hoop of the world. Sometimes they called it the sacred hoop. He sang songs to the spirits and gave up his prayers to the Great Mystery. That's how they called it, *Wakan Tanka*, the Great Mystery."

"And what about the vision?"

"That's what he was hoping for. Mostly it would be in the shape of some animal that came to him and talked to him, or taught him a song, or showed him some special thing for his medicine bag . . . to bring him power. That spirit was supposed to be his spirit helper . . . to call on when he needed power. After the three days was up, the medicine man collected the boy and led him back to camp. The boy told his vision so it could be explained. Usually he got a new name according to whatever his vision was. Made him one of a kind."

"What's it look like, you suppose?"

"Oh, I guess it's close to being a dream."

"Did your grandfather ever have one?"

Clete studied the distance for a moment, considering. "I don't know," he said slowly. "There was troubled times when he was a boy. The government was roping off the reservations and putting down the Indian ceremonies,

384

except when they sneaked in one the government didn't hear about. But otherwise they were pretty much cut off from the way they'd been living.

"I guess my granddad knew about the vision quests from the old people. Sometimes I used to wonder . . . he could make it sound so real. He had a name, Alvin Running Moon, but I never knew if it was a vision name or if he earned it in some special way as a boy. Never know now. A man ought to know, but I don't."

Sam let the story float in his mind. From being a boy into being a man, that'd be something. Being your own self . . . one of a kind . . . finding your own power. The possibilities grew.

"Suppose I could do that?" he asked suddenly.

"What?" Clete was yawning.

"Go on one. A vision quest."

A snort of amusement. "What for?"

"I could use some magic power. Some days I don't seem to count for much."

Clete groaned. "I'm gonna call you Sam Many Troubles. You ache where you ain't even got muscles."

Sam straightened up at that, frowning, and stretched his long legs out before him. His scuffed shoes reminded him of the work waiting. The heat and heaviness washed over him.

As if sensing Sam's mood, Clete said, "Oh, I don't say it wasn't as good a way as any to grow up, getting hitched to some vision idea, wanting something magical. But you still got to add the sweat by yourself. Me, I've done plenty of sweating, but it didn't amount to a hoot." He slumped back and drew the hat over his eyes.

"Aw, Clete, don't say that."

"I already did."

385

"It sounds like science fiction or another planet . . . all those visions," Sam said.

"It does, in a manner," said Clete drowsily, "but, shoot, they lived right around here. Up north by the mountains you can still see tepee rings from a camp. Plenty of dreams and magic in those mountains, you bet." His voice trailed off.

Sam thought of his mountain mirage. Once he'd seen the image of faraway mountaintops, hanging low in the sky, sharp and close. Ordinarily the peaks were only dark humps in the north, but some mystery of the air had floated them up that day, like a promise of things cool and high and inviting. Sam still remembered it whenever he wished he could be somewhere else. Which was often. It was almost a vision, he decided, except it didn't give him any power.

"Maybe we should go up and see those tepee rings sometime," Sam said. There was no response, so he tapped Clete on the shoulder. "How about that?"

"Not today," Clete mumbled. "I'm uncommonly tired today. Don't need vision dreams so much as sleeping ones. Gimme time."

"Okay," Sam said. He stood up and moved away so as not to bother Clete. The vision story was still in his mind, and the rippling image still washed low against the prairie. Wish it was a real lake, he thought, so I could take a swim.

No . . . be better if it was a vision . . . to help me over the rough spots . . . make me strong as a daylong runner. That'd be a wonderful magic.

He decided then and there that someday he would make a vision quest of his own.

386

Jorinda and Joringel
THE BROTHERS GRIMM

Translated by
ELIZABETH SHUB

Once there was an ancient castle that stood in the midst of a great, dense forest. In the castle, all alone, lived an old woman who was a witch. In the daytime she was a cat or a screech-owl, but when night came she always took the shape of a human being again. She lured wild beasts and birds to the castle and killed them to boil or roast.

Should a man or boy come within a hundred paces of where she lived, he was immediately rooted to the spot, until the witch chose to set him free. If it happened that a maiden stepped within the enchanted park, the witch would turn her into a bird and put her in a wicker cage, which she placed in a special room. She had about seven thousand of these rare birds imprisoned in the castle.

There was a maiden called Jorinda, who was very beautiful. She and a handsome youth called Joringel were engaged to be married, and their greatest joy was to be together. One day, in order to discuss some important matters in private, they decided to go for a walk in the forest.

"We must be careful," warned Joringel, "not to go too near the castle." It was a beautiful afternoon. The sun's rays shone brightly between the tree trunks, piercing the deep green of the forest. From the old birch branches came the doleful song of a turtledove.

387

But it was not long before Jorinda and Joringel realized that they were lost and could not find their way home. They were beside themselves. Every now and then they would sit down in the sunshine in utter despair. Only half the setting sun still showed above the mountain. Then Joringel peered through the bushes, and when he saw the old walls of the castle nearby, he was terrified.

Jorinda had begun to sing:

> *My little bird has a necklace red*
> *And sings sorrow, sorrow, sorrow.*
> *He sings the dove will soon be dead,*
> *Sings sorrow, sor–tsikit, tsikit, tsikit. . .*

Joringel looked for Jorinda and saw only a nightingale singing "tsikit, tsikit. . ." A screech-owl with glowing eyes flew three times around her, each time crying, "schu, hu, hu, hu!" Joringel stood as if turned to stone. He could neither move nor speak.

The sun had set. The owl flew behind a thicket and out came a crooked old woman, yellow and thin, with large red eyes and a hooked nose. Muttering to herself, she caught the

388

nightingale and carried it away in her hand. Joringel could only watch the nightingale being taken away.

At last the old woman returned and in a gloomy voice chanted:

> *Greetings, Zachiel, hail to thee.*
> *Unspell Joringel, set him free.*
> *Moonbeams warm Jorinda's basket.*
> *Loose him now, because I ask it.*

Joringel at once felt himself free. He fell on his knees before the old woman and implored her to give Jorinda back to him. But the old woman swore that he would never see Jorinda again and, turning away, took herself off to the castle. Joringel called after her, begged and pleaded, but all in vain.

He wandered about until at last he came to a strange village, where he decided to remain and become a shepherd. He often returned to the vicinity of the castle, circling the grounds, always careful not to come too close.

At last, one night he dreamed that he found a blood-red flower, in the center of which rested a beautiful large pearl. In his dream he picked the flower and went to the castle, and everything he touched with it was no longer enchanted. He also dreamed that with the flower he rescued Jorinda.

In the morning when he awoke, he began to search over hill and dale for a flower such as the one he had found in his dream. He searched for eight days and nights and early on the morning of the ninth day, he found it. In its center was a dewdrop as large as a pearl. Taking the flower with him, he journeyed to the castle.

When he was a hundred paces from it, Joringel was overjoyed to see that the spell no longer held and that he could continue on. He reached the castle gate, touched it with the flower, and it sprang open.

Once in the courtyard, he paused and listened for the sound of birds. Hearing them twittering and singing, he followed the voices until he came to a room where the old woman was busy feeding her birds in their seven thousand cages.

When she saw Joringel, she grew so angry she spat bile and venom and spumed in fury, but she could not come within two paces of him.

He paid no attention to her and instead went from cage to cage seeking Jorinda. There were hundreds of nightingales; how was he to find her?

Just then he noticed through the corner of his eye that the witch had picked up a cage and was making for the door.

He ran swiftly to her, touched the cage with the flower and also touched the witch, who was at once deprived of her magic power. Jorinda, as beautiful as ever, stood before him and threw her arms around his neck.

After changing all the other birds into maidens again, Joringel went home with Jorinda, and they lived contentedly ever after.

Questions at Night

Why
Is the sky?

What starts the thunder overhead?
Who makes the crashing noise?
Are the angels falling out of bed?
Are they breaking all their toys?

Why does the sun go down so soon?
Why do the night-clouds crawl
Hungrily up to the new-laid moon
And swallow it, shell and all?

If there's a Bear among the stars
As all the people say,
Won't he jump over those Pasture-bars
And drink up the Milky Way?

Does every star that happens to fall
Turn into a fire-fly?
Can't it ever get back to Heaven at all?
And why
Is the sky?

—Louis Untermeyer

391

Maria's Comet

KATHARINE E. WILKIE

Maria Mitchell grew up on the island of Nantucket, twenty miles off the Massachusetts coast, in the 1800s. Her Quaker father had been a farmer, a teacher, and a bank cashier, but his great love was astronomy.

When she was ten years old, Maria was helping her father set the chronometers that the Nantucket sea captains used to determine their positions at sea. She was also sharing his observations of the stars and planets through a telescope at the top of their house.

Maria wanted to go to college, but in 1836 very few colleges admitted women. Her family could not afford to send her to college anyway. So she took the job of librarian at the Atheneum, the island's library.

It had been a long day at the Atheneum. Maria found a half-dozen guests in the parlor when she returned home.

She soon left them and slipped away to the housetop. It was a perfect autumn night for sweeping the skies. She looked at the logbook and noted what she and her father had done the night before.

She turned the telescope and . looked at Orion. Then through the lens she sighted the star group called the Corona Borealis.

Downstairs she could hear laughter and talking. She was tired, and glad to be up here alone with the stars.

Suddenly she stiffened. There in the upper part of the field of the telescope was a tiny white spot. She knew that part of the heavens as well as she knew the Atheneum. No white spot should be there.

She turned her head and closed her eyes. Could they be tricking her?

She looked again through the lens. The white spot was still there.

The chronometer showed that the time was exactly half past ten. She wrote down the figures.

Then she rose and hurried down

the narrow attic stairs to find her
father. She must be sure!

The guests stopped talking as she
rushed into the room. Mr. Mitchell
looked up.

"Come quickly, Father!" she
urged.

She turned and flew back up the
stairs. Father was close behind.
Mother, sister Kate, and the guests
followed.

Up on the rooftop William
Mitchell looked carefully through
the lens. He shook his head and
turned away. Then he looked again
for a long time.

With a proud smile he turned to
the others and spoke. "My friends, I
believe my daughter has discovered a
new comet on this night of October
1, 1847."

393

That night Mr. Mitchell wrote to his old friend, Professor William Bond, at Harvard University.

Before long a letter from the professor arrived. He had used Maria's reckoning and found the comet with his telescope.

Father waved the letter. "I told thee! Soon the whole world will be hearing of thy comet."

"Do not call it *my* comet," Maria answered.

"Why not? A comet is always named for the person who discovers it. Thee will soon be hearing more.

Professor Bond has sent a notice to a German journal which announces all such discoveries."

Day after day passed. At last Father had another letter.

"Just listen to this!" he exclaimed. "Professor Bond writes: 'It seems that Maria Mitchell's comet has not been seen before in Europe.' " He looked proudly at his daughter. "Twenty-nine years old and already you have become a famous astronomer!"

"Thee has taught me all I know," Maria told him. "It is as much thy discovery as mine."

Mother interrupted. "Whenever thee stop admiring each other, there is work to be done." But she looked proud too.

In 1831 the king of Denmark had promised a gold medal to the first discoverer of a "telescopic comet." This kind of comet is visible only through a telescope.

Was Maria the first to announce the discovery of the comet? There seemed some doubt. Her father's letter had been delayed by a storm. The ship carrying the mail left Nantucket three days after Maria's discovery. A man in Rome had seen the comet on October third. Who had announced it first?

Even the president of Harvard was drawn into the question. So was the Astronomer Royal of Great Britain. So were other important people in America and Denmark.

At last, on October 6, 1848, the king of Denmark awarded the medal to Maria. It was a great day for her when it arrived in a little velvet box.

There were tears in her eyes as she looked at it. On one side of the medal was the likeness of the king of Denmark. On the other side in Latin were the words "Not in vain do we watch the setting and rising of the stars."

Under the words was the date October 1, 1847. MARIA MITCHELL was printed in large letters around the edge.

"Now thee is beginning thy career," William Mitchell told her.

She shook her head. "I began it long ago when thee first taught me the wonder of the stars."

The Art of Marc Chagall

ERNEST RABOFF

Marc Chagall was born on July 7, 1887, in a small Russian village called Vitebsk. Zahar Chagall, his father, worked in a herring-packing house. His son remembers him as a tall, quiet and shy man who was always working. Feiga-Ita, his mother, had eight other children besides her oldest son Marc. She had a small shop in her home where she sold herring, flour, sugar, and spices to add to the family income.

Chagall moved to France in 1923. From 1941 until 1948, he lived in the United States. Then he returned to France. But it was the dreamlike memories of Russia that he mostly painted and for which he is famous.

About painting, Marc Chagall said, "It was more necessary for me than food. It seemed to me like a window through which I could have taken flight toward another world."

Vase of Flowers by Moonlight (at the right) glows like an outdoor fire in the blue of the night sky. The bouquet fills the night with color and fragrance. The sounds of the evening are represented by the violinist in the upper left corner. The animal on the roof seems to be a symbol of security and peace. The moon is reflected in a halo of light around the resting animal's head.

Vase of Flowers by Moonlight (1943)

I And The Village is as much fun as it is beautiful. The eye of the cow, centered in the picture, sees many things. Within its head is the vision of itself with the milkmaid. Outside itself it is aware of a person facing it, perhaps the artist.

In the lower left corner the sun and the moon are combined and repeat a pattern that makes a diagonal path across the picture. In the upper right side a priest stands in the doorway of his church.

Chagall shows us the village from many points of view, right side up and upside down. The happiness of the artist and of the life of the village is shown by the colorful beads worn by the cow, and by the smile on the lips of the person at the right.

Time Is A River Without Banks should be studied to explore the full meaning of the title.

The curious flying fish playing the violin reflects the color and flames of the sun on its wings and mouth. On one bank of the river is a young couple who are unaware of the grandfather clock ticking away the hours. They hear only the music.

On the other side, curving around the horizon, are the houses of the city. They stand silently, holding the history of time and the river in their worn bricks and stone walls.

The blue of the day and the darker blue of the night fill the canvas with color. A lone fisherman paddles his way into the future.

399

Dreams

Hold fast to dreams
For if dreams die
Life is a broken-winged bird
That cannot fly.

Hold fast to dreams
For when dreams go
Life is a barren field
Frozen with snow.

—Langston Hughes

Plain Old Grace Jones, Farewell!

JANE LANGTON

The seat of the old wicker chair on the rock was worn right through. Grace had found that she could make herself fairly comfortable by sinking down in it until her knees were level with her chest. She sank down into it now, with a whoosh, and opened her scrapbook of the British Royal Family.

The question was, did she, Grace Jones, show a family resemblance to the crowned heads of the British Empire? Was she, could she be, a royal princess?

There was a loose sheet of paper in the front of the scrapbook. On it was a written list. Grace frowned. What was that doing here?

The Six Falts of Grace Jones
1. I am messie.   *4. I bite my fingernales.*
2. I am clumsy.   *5. I am mean to my little sister.*
3. I cannot spell.   *6. I cry.*

That list described the old Grace Jones—the plain, ordinary one. The new one wasn't like that at all! Grace quickly turned the page.

This was what she was looking for. The rest of the scrapbook was filled with Grace's newspaper clippings about the new King of England, George VI, and his family. Most of the clippings were photographs of his two little girls. Grace breathed hard and studied the pictures of Princess Elizabeth and Princess Margaret Rose.

401

Did they have round faces and brown hair, like Grace? Did they have thin legs and snub noses? The scrapbook rested on Grace's knees, and since her knees were wedged against her chest, she could see the photographs at close range. The vague faces of the princesses dissolved into thousands of gray dots. Were they anything like Grace's face? Grace couldn't be sure.

But the proofs of her royal lineage were so strong! Grace stared down the hill at the B&O Railroad tracks and went over the list of proofs in her mind. The first proof was what that new girl had said, on the very day the Jones family moved from Boston, Massachusetts, to Cleveland, Ohio. No sooner had the Joneses finished the long journey from Boston, and driven down the dusty lane to the new house, and climbed wearily out of Petunia, their old Model-A Ford, and stood on the grass looking up at their new front porch, than the girl from next door had walked right down the lane to say hello. She had stared at Grace, and then she had said that wonderful thing. Turning her head to one side and looking at Grace with half-closed eyes, she had said, "You know what? You look just like Princess Elizabeth."

"Oh, I do not either," said Grace, surprised and pleased.

Grace leaned back now in the wicker chair and held up one finger. That was the first proof. The second was what her own mother had said, just a few minutes ago, while she was unpacking dishes to store in the cupboards of the new house. Mom had been telling Will and Sophie where they were born. It turned out that they were both born in Boston.

"Well, where was I born?" Grace had wanted to know. "In Boston too?"

"You weren't born in the United States at all," said Mom. "You were born in British territory."

"What?" said Grace. But before she could find out what her mother meant, the telephone rang and Mom ran to answer it. It was just the telephone company checking the line. By the time her mother had hung the receiver back on the hook and come back to the barrel of dishes, Grace had wandered away. She had felt the dreamy beginnings of her glorious idea. Could it be? Was she really?

Grace held up her second finger. Two solid proofs that she was! If she looked like Princess Elizabeth and if she had been born on British soil, perhaps she wasn't the child of Mr. and Mrs. Joseph Jones at all. Perhaps she was someone very much more important. Perhaps she had been left on the Joneses' front doorstep in a basket by the British royal family! Perhaps she was really a royal princess of England!

Folded up in the wicker chair, Grace felt dizzy with discovery. She held her hands up toward the sun and looked at them proudly. The sunlight shone through the edges of her fingers, making them glow pink. What was that gushing through her veins? Royal blood!

The old chair on the rock was perched high above the ground, at the top of the hill in front of the new house. Far below the rock, at the bottom of the field, ran the railroad tracks. Beside the rock grew a tree with long black seed pods. The seed pods looked just like cigars. Grace reached up excitedly and picked a cigar. She held it between two fingers and pretended to puff on it.

There was another question. If she were a member of the royal family, would she still be a middle child? Grace turned back to her scrapbook and pored over it again. She found an article that gave the princesses' birthdays and ages. No, she was older than Princess Elizabeth. Grace's eyes widened. That was very important. It meant that she, Grace Jones, was the heir to the throne! A royal princess and the future Queen of England!

The glory of it was overwhelming. Grace put her hands on the arms of the chair and gazed down the hill. She saw before her, not the field and the railroad tracks, but the golden walls of a lofty hall. The wicker chair had suddenly become a throne, and the rock was Buckingham Palace.

"Ask me how to spell *nonentity*," said Grace's big brother, Will. Grace jumped. She hadn't even heard him bumping his old black bicycle down the hill and up the sloping side of the rock.

"Ask you how to spell what?" said Grace.

"*Nonentity*," said Will. "It means somebody plain and ordinary, just like everybody else. Ask me how to spell it."

"O.K.," said Grace, "spell it."

"Nonentity," said Will. "N-O-N-E-N-T-I-T-Y."

Grace knew better than to argue with Will's spelling. "Very good," she said, looking back at her scrapbook. It was amazing the way Will could spell anything. He was always right. He was as good as a dictionary. In one way, though, his spelling wasn't so amazing. Will always said that he could see the words in his mind just the way they looked on the pages of a book. Then all he had to do was read them from the page in his mind, letter by letter. So, really, all he had to do was read. Anybody could spell if they had a picture of the word in their mind to read.

Will propped his bike against the side of the rock and reached up for a cigar. "Ask me how to spell *cigar*," said Will, wondering how it was spelled.

"Oh, go ahead and spell *cigar*," said Grace. She was tired of the way everybody admired Will for his spelling.

Will looked at the cigar-shaped pod in his hand, and let his mind go blank like a white page. There were letters forming on it. "C-I-G-A-R, cigar," read Will.

Grace squirmed up out of the wicker chair. She had just thought of a difficult problem. *Why* had the British royal family hidden away the true heir to the throne in the United States? Grace wanted to get away from Will and think this question over.

405

"Can I borrow your bike?" she asked Will. She jumped down and dropped her scrapbook into the bicycle basket.

"What for?" said Will. "You don't even know how to ride a bike yet."

Of course she knew how to ride a bike. The future Queen of England could do practically anything. She'd show Will. Grace grabbed the handlebars and lowered the bike to the ground. She was too short to reach her leg over the crossbar, so she climbed part of the way back up the rock and jumped recklessly astride the saddle. The bicycle moved forward, wobbling in the tall grass. It was heading downhill. "Farewell," cried Grace dramatically. "Farewell to plain old Grace Jones!"

"Hey, watch out!" yelled Will.

It was too late now. Grace's legs flailed the air, fighting for balance. The bicycle was going faster and faster, gaining momentum, lurching between thorny bushes and stones. Grace clung for dear life to the handlebars. She tried to find the pedals with her feet, and almost tipped over. That wouldn't do. She needed her feet thrown out sideways for balance. Her bones shook and her teeth chattered as the bike jounced from bump to bump. How could she ever stop it? She could hear Will shouting and chasing her, but something was making so much noise she couldn't make out what he was saying. The bike was racing now, abandoned to gravity, plunging toward the railroad tracks at the bottom of the hill.

The railroad tracks! That noise was a B&O train, and she was headed right across its path!

Grace tried to throw herself off the bike, but it was going so fast that now she couldn't lose her balance even though she wanted to. She gave herself up for lost. But even in her last moments she found time to imagine a wistful scene. She, Grace, was lying in a velvet-lined coffin in Westminster Abbey while the whole population of the British Isles filed reverently by, gazing with sorrow at the beautiful young princess who was never to take her rightful place upon the throne.

Bump-splash! The bike ground to a stop in a muddy hollow between some swampy hummocks of grass at the bottom of the hill and turned over on its side. Grace continued to fly forward through the air, coming down, not too hard, on all fours in the mud. She lay there for a minute, watching the train roar by.

The engineer hadn't even seen her. Grace realized that she wouldn't have ridden across the tracks anyway, because an embankment lifted them several feet above the bottom of the field.

She rolled over and examined herself. Her legs were scratched by the bristly thickets she had ridden through, and one knee was bleeding where it had landed on a stone. She leaned forward and sucked the place.

Will stood with folded arms and looked at her.

"Don't tell," said Grace.

Will lifted his bike in a dignified way, handed Grace her scrapbook and started back uphill. "You certainly made a fool of yourself," said Will.

That Will! He'd be sorry when he found out who Grace really was. She picked herself up and started to limp up the hill after her brother. Mom was whistling for lunch. The answer to Grace's problem had just occurred to her.

Of course! It was just like King Arthur. The reason the King and Queen of England had been forced to hide Grace away in the United States was that there had been a plot to murder her, their first-born child. King Arthur, too, had been hidden away in the country until he grew up, so that he would be safe from the wicked lords who wanted to kill him so that one of them could be the next king.

Grace hobbled on. But who, she wondered, would want to kill her? Maybe it was the Duke of Gloucester. Grace's royal parents must have been warned against him, and they had decided to protect the baby's life by having it brought up secretly in the United States by some worthy couple. They had chosen Mr. and Mrs.

Joseph Jones to be the foster parents of the future Queen of England.

She, Grace, the future Queen of England! What difference did it make, thought Grace happily, if a person couldn't spell and had a lot of other faults, if she were a queen?

Grace plumped herself down at the kitchen table. She looked at her mother and smiled tenderly. When she was queen she would continue to love both her foster parents, of course, just as if she were still plain old Grace Jones back in the U.S.A.

Grace's mother slapped a serving dish on the table, then hurried back to the stove. "Grace," she said, "why do I always have to tell you to go and wash first?"

Grace went upstairs to the bathroom and sprinkled cold water on her hands and face. When Grace got back to the table, Mrs. Jones took a closer look at her. "Grace," she said, "where on earth have you been? Look at those knees! You wash those knees before you come to the table."

Grace looked at the serving dishes. Hot dogs and baked beans—her favorite meal. Oh, well. She ran upstairs again. While she splashed cold water on the washcloth and rubbed at her knees, she could hear Will downstairs saying, "Ask me how to spell *cigar*."

Grace rubbed and rubbed. It was no use. She was just naturally the messy sort of person that dirt stuck to. She could hear her father come up into the kitchen from the cellar, where he had been unpacking his mineral collection. He said, "That's right! That's very good, Will." Long drips of water were running down Grace's legs, making clean streaks in the gray, and her knee stung where the hurt place was wet. That will just have to do, she decided, and ran downstairs once more. She gave her father a radiant smile and sat down.

Pop looked at her. Then he put down his serving spoon and said to Mom, "When did that child last have a bath?"

Mom looked at Grace and shook her head. "Believe it or not, it was just last night," she said. "Dirt just seems to stick to Grace."

"Look at her neck," said Pop. He was staring at Grace. Everybody was staring at Grace—even little Sophie. "Grace," said Pop, "you go right upstairs and don't you come down again to this table until you're clean. Understand?"

Grace stood up. Her lip trembled. She felt stiff all over. She walked to the door. Then she turned around. "What do you think I am—a nonennity?" she cried. "I'll have you know you're talking to the future Queen of England!" Then she ran up the stairs and into her room and slammed the door and flung herself on her bed.

Downstairs at the table Mr. Jones looked at his wife with his mouth open. Then he said, "What's the matter with that girl now?"

"Oh, I don't know," said Mrs. Jones. "She must be making up stories about herself again, and now you've hurt her feelings."

Mom got up and went upstairs to Grace's room. She knocked on the door.

"Come in," said a muffled voice.

"Grace, dear, what is it?" said her mother, sitting down beside her on the bed and patting her on the back.

"Oh, gee whiz," said Grace.

"Pop loves you, dear," said Mom, "clean or dirty. Come on in the bathroom now and I'll help you get clean."

It was all right, decided Grace, cheering up. How could they be expected to know? There she had been on the doorstep, just a baby in a basket! How could her mother and father be expected to treat her like a royal princess?

While her mother let the water run hot and scrubbed at Grace's knees and neck, Grace patiently stood stock still. As she went downstairs for the third time, she felt filled with a generous and noble forgiveness. She sat down at the table with a thump and attacked her baked beans.

"Would Her Royal Highness like some ketchup?" asked Pop.

"Sure," said the future Queen of England.

"Ask me how to spell *ketchup*," said Will.

The Nightingale

HANS CHRISTIAN ANDERSEN

Long ago the emperor of China had the most beautiful palace in the world. It was made entirely of the finest porcelain and was surrounded by a garden full of extraordinary flowers. This garden was so big that even the gardener did not know where it ended.

At the edge of the flowers beautiful woods with lofty trees and deep lakes began. The woods extended to the sea. Among these trees lived a nightingale which sang so beautifully that all the fishermen kept still and listened to it when they were out at night drawing in their nets.

Travelers came to the emperor's capital from every country in the world. Some wrote books about the town, the palace, and the garden. But the nightingale was always put above everything else.

These books went all over the world, and in time some of them reached the emperor. He was well pleased to hear such beautiful descriptions of the palace and the garden. "But the nightingale is the best of all," he read.

"What is this?" said the emperor. "The nightingale? Why, I know nothing about it. Is there such a bird in my kingdom, even in my own garden, and I have never heard of it?"

Then he called his gentleman-in-waiting. "There is said to be a very wonderful bird called a nightingale here," said the emperor. "The books say that it is better than anything else in all my kingdom! Why have I never been told anything about it?"

"I have never heard it mentioned," said the gentleman-in-waiting. "It has never been presented at court."

"I wish to have it appear here this evening to sing to me," said the emperor. "The whole world knows what I have, and I know nothing about it!"

But where could the nightingale be found? The gentleman-in-waiting ran upstairs and downstairs and in and out of all the rooms and hallways. No one he met had ever heard anything about the nightingale.

"But I will hear this nightingale," said the emperor. "I insist on having it here tonight. I offer my most gracious protection to it. And if it is not here, I will have the whole court trampled on after supper!"

"Tsing-poo!" said the gentleman-in-waiting, and away he ran again, up and down all the stairs and in and out of all the rooms and hallways. Half the court ran with him, for none of them wished to be trampled on.

At last they talked to a girl in the kitchen. She said, "Oh, the nightingale? I know it very well. Yes, indeed it can sing. Every evening I go down by the shore. On my way back, when I am tired, I rest awhile in the woods, and then I hear the nightingale. Its song brings tears to my eyes!"

"Can you take us to the nightingale?" asked the gentleman-in-waiting. "It is supposed to appear at court tonight."

So they all went into the woods where the nightingale usually sang. The girl led them to a place deep in the trees. Then the nightingale began to sing.

"There it is!" said the girl. "Listen, listen! There it is." And she pointed to the nightingale, sitting on the branch of a nearby tree.

413

"Is it possible?" said the gentleman-in-waiting. "I should never have thought it was like that. It looks so plain! Seeing so many people must have frightened all its colors away." He approached the nightingale.

"My precious little nightingale," he said, "I have the honor to ask you to attend a court festival tonight, where you will charm His Gracious Majesty the emperor with your fascinating singing."

"It sounds best among the trees," said the nightingale. But it went with them willingly when it heard that the emperor wished it.

The palace had been brightened up for the occasion. The walls and the floors, which were all of china, shone by the light of many thousand golden lamps. The most beautiful flowers, all of the tinkling kind, were arranged in the hallways.

In the middle of the large reception room where the emperor sat, a golden rod had been fixed, on which the nightingale was to perch. The whole court was assembled. They were all dressed in their best. Everybody's eyes were turned toward the little gray bird.

The nightingale sang delightfully, and tears came into the emperor's eyes. They rolled down his cheeks. The nightingale sang more beautifully than ever. Its notes touched all hearts. The emperor was charmed and said the nightingale should have his gold slipper to wear around its neck. But the nightingale declined with thanks; it had already been sufficiently rewarded.

"I have seen tears in the eyes of the emperor. That is my richest reward. Tears of an emperor have a wonderful power! I am sufficiently repaid!" It again burst into its sweet song.

The nightingale was a sensation. It was supposed to stay

414

at court and have its own cage, as well as liberty to go out twice a day and once in the night. But it was always accompanied by twelve footmen, each holding a ribbon which was tied around its leg.

The whole town talked about the marvelous bird. If two people met, one said to the other, "Night," and the other answered, "Gale." Then they sighed, understanding each other perfectly.

One day a large parcel came for the emperor. It was a gift from the emperor of Japan. In the box was an artificial nightingale exactly like the living one, except that it was studded all over with diamonds, rubies, and sapphires.

When the bird was wound up, it sang one of the songs the real nightingale sang, and it wagged its tail, which glittered with silver and gold. Everybody said, "Oh, how beautiful!"

The artificial bird was just as great a success as the real one, and it was much prettier to look at. It sang the same tune over and over, and yet it was not tired.

People wanted to hear it from the beginning again, but the emperor said that the real bird must have a turn now. But where was it? No one had noticed that the real nightingale had flown out the open window, back to its own green woods.

"But what is the meaning of this?" asked the emperor.

All the people in the court said it was a most ungrateful bird. "We have the best bird though," they said. Then the artificial bird began to sing again. The real nightingale was banished from the kingdom.

The artificial bird had its place on a silken cushion close to the emperor's bed. Its place was on the emperor's left side, for the emperor thought that the side where the heart was located was the important one.

415

Things went on in this way for a whole year. The emperor, the court, and the rest of the people knew every little gurgle in the song of the artificial bird by heart, but they liked it even more because of this, for they could all join in the song themselves.

But one evening when the bird was singing its best and the emperor was lying in bed listening to it, something gave way inside the bird with a *whizz*. Then a spring broke; *whirr* went all the wheels. The music stopped.

The emperor jumped out of bed and sent for his private physicians. But what good could they do? Then he sent for the watchmaker, who after a good deal of talk and examination, got the works to go again somehow. But he warned that the bird would have to be used very carefully because it was so worn out.

This was a great blow to the emperor and the people! They could only let the artificial bird sing once a year.

Five years passed, and a great grief came upon the nation. The emperor lay pale and cold in his big bed. He was not dead yet, although he could hardly breathe. He seemed to have a weight on his chest. He opened his eyes, and then he saw that it was Death sitting upon his chest.

"Music, music!" shrieked the emperor. "You precious little golden bird, sing, sing that I may drive Death away."

But the bird stood silent. There was nobody to wind it up, so it could not go. Death continued to fix its great empty eye sockets upon the emperor. All was silent, so terribly silent.

Suddenly, close to the open window of the emperor's room, there was a burst of lovely song. It was the live nightingale, perched on a branch outside. It had heard of the emperor's need and had come to bring comfort and hope to him. The nightingale sang and sang, until Death flew out the window.

"Thank you, thank you!" said the emperor. "You heavenly little bird. I know you! I banished you from my kingdom, and yet you have charmed Death away from my bed with your song. How can I ever repay you?"

"You have rewarded me," said the nightingale. "I brought tears to your eyes the very first time I ever sang to you, and I shall never forget it!"

"You must always stay with me!" said the emperor. "You shall only sing when you like."

"I can't build my nest and live in this palace," said the nightingale, "but let me come whenever I like, and I will sit on the branch in the evening and sing to you."

Then the nightingale flew away. The attendants came in to see their dead emperor. And there he stood to say, "Good morning!"

Theater of the Night

S. CARL HIRSCH

You walk into a darkened theater and take your seat. For some time you sit in drowsy comfort, cradled by the silence and the shadows.

Then the curtain rises. The action begins—and what a play it is! Performers come and go, one of them remarkably like yourself. There is little sense to what is being said, and less to what is being done.

In aimless fashion the story unfolds. The plot is sheer fantasy. The players are busy with a lot of puzzling nonsense that leads nowhere. And yet it all seems real as life. Abruptly the play comes to an end.

You will learn in time that you yourself were the producer, playwright, and director. The scenery, the props, the cast—they were all your own creations. But mysteriously, you understand little of what was going on!

This was a dream. For all its puzzling qualities, this was no rare or extraordinary event. In fact, the most remarkable feature of a dream is that it is the common and usual experience of everyone. We share this nightly occurrence with the people of the entire world, and with those who have lived in every age. All of us are regular patrons of this same theater.

The next show? Yes, of course, it will be presented tonight. Admission is free. What's more, you won't even have to leave your warm bed.

Calvin Hall, an American scientist studying dreams, felt that if enough dreams could be gathered and studied, a pattern would emerge. So back in the 1940s, this early specialist in dreams became a tireless collector.

It was Hall's own dream that this dream bank would represent a wide range of nighttime thoughts. The collection would include the dreams of old, middle-aged, and young people of both sexes and of many backgrounds. Hall was seeking what he called "the dreams of normal people."

Many dreams were provided by volunteers in his own sleep laboratories in Miami, Florida, and Santa Cruz, California. He also sought written dream records from research centers throughout the world. In time his institute had a stock of fifty thousand dreams.

The information poured in from widely separated sources. One study that was fed into Hall's computers compared seven thousand dreams of students—half of them Japanese, the other half American. Also in Hall's collection were the night visions of Peruvian mountaineers, Nigerian tribesmen, Irish fisher folk, Eskimo seal hunters. Dream details pictured the land and customs of various groups. Yet these very different accounts contained many common themes—among them birth and death, quest and discovery, triumph and defeat. Dreams of traveling, facing danger, finding treasure, floating in space, struggling with enemies, suffering frustration were

also common. So were dreams of being chased, lost, saved, loved, and hated.

To classify this huge collection, Hall organized the dreams according to content. Who were the people taking part in the dream story and what were they doing? What objects appeared and in what setting? What were the events that occurred in the dream? Did it have a happy ending or a sad one?

Analysis of the subject matter of the collected dreams revealed a few surprises. People do not ordinarily dream about the news of the day, foreign affairs, well-known people, or the outcome of elections. Nor do they commonly dream about their jobs, their studies, their household chores, church, or community activities. Instead, dreams are much more personal.

The dreamer may be central and active in the "plot," or may simply be a spectator or bystander. And while the "cast of characters" often includes friends or members of the dreamer's own family, Hall discovered that four out of every ten characters in dreams are strangers to the dreamer. Others may be people seen or met casually in the dim past.

What goes on in the dream? The dreamer is often in the midst of some kind of movement or local travel—riding, walking, running, jumping, climbing. A great many dreams are quiet, with the characters talking, sitting, or watching. Less often, the dreamer is taking part in some activity. These are samples:

"I dreamed I was a shepherd tending a flock of big ladybugs."

"I was driving into a busy intersection, but the brakes of the car wouldn't work."

"I put a nickel in the slot machine and out poured a jackpot of dirty dishes."

Often dreams are quite dull. But the dreaming mind is a storyteller, and the "plots" may be simple or complex, drawn-out or brief, factual or fantastic. And though many dreams are too slight to recount, others are rich in action, humor, color, and excitement. This is the

type we usually hear about when someone sits down to breakfast saying, "Listen, I just had the craziest dream. . . ."

Dreams begin in the middle. We find ourselves involved in a situation, a conflict, a crisis.

"I turned on this big fireman's hose, but I can't shut it off."

"I am kissing my cousin whom I don't really like."

"I can't find my way out of a dark cave full of bats with flashing eyes."

"I am flying over the city in a beautiful glider when I know I should be down below minding my baby sister."

Sometimes the setting itself is an important part of the dream. We are at a school picnic or a stock car race. We are in a Persian mosque, a funeral home, or a scene straight out of a recent TV program or book we've read.

"I am talking to three corpses in the county morgue."

"I was riding a motorcycle backward up the side of a mountain."

"My friend and I are rummaging

through a trunk full of old dolls."

"I was swimming in a pool when the water suddenly turned into raspberry Jell-O."

The dreamer is rarely alone. Usually several others are present. The dream sometimes draws on events long-forgotten. But often it is based on something that happened the day before—even though the dream version may be so scrambled that the events are hardly recognizable. Some of the people may be unknown, and often they do and say the strangest things.

Our dreams sometimes come in series. At least, there are objects, persons, or events in them that may reappear. Sometimes these chains occur in the dreams of one night. Or a person's dreams over a period of time may be linked together by common themes, patterns, or moods.

"Sweet dreams!" is a common good-night wish. But many dreams are not sweet or pleasant. In our sleeping adventures we are often lost, hunted, or searching for someone or something. There may be a frustrating sense of not being able to make oneself heard or of trying to remember some lost but important fact. We find ourselves in some conflict involving good and evil, or else we seek pleasure while feeling pain.

Unfortunately, the problem in the dream usually remains unsolved. Things do not often wind their way to a neat conclusion as they do in storybooks. We may be awakened just as it seems that matters are about to be settled. However, even one more hour of sleep may not allow us to complete a chapter or save us from danger.

According to one well-known theory, all dreaming is a kind of wishful thinking. Supposedly, the visions of the night satisfy the hopes of the day. A popular song of years ago expressed the idea this way: "A dream is a wish your heart makes. . . ."

If only that were true! Some dreams are pleasant. But often we awake puzzled or frightened. At such times we are grateful for the ringing alarm clock and thankful that it was "only a dream!"

Jahdu and the Magic Power

VIRGINIA HAMILTON

Mama Luka liked to sit in her tight little room in a fine, good place called Harlem. She liked to sit with the window blinds drawn against the sunlight. And Mama Luka did, every day.

Mama Luka had black skin and a nose as curved as the beak of a parrot. She wore her hair in one long pigtail down her back. She called the pigtail her plait, and she could sit on it. She sat on it whenever she felt like telling tales.

Mama Luka took care of Lee Edward after his school was out for the day and until his mother came home from work. And Mama Luka sat all the while in her little room in the good place, telling Jahdu stories to Lee Edward. She told them slow and she told them easy. And Lee Edward listened. He sat on the floor with his eyes tight shut, which was the best way for him to imagine Jahdu.

Lee Edward loved Mama Luka. She sometimes called him Little Brother just like his own mama did. And he loved his own mama, who worked. He loved his papa, too, who worked when he could. Lee Edward loved Jahdu and Jahdu stories. And he loved the way Mama Luka told them like any boy would.

"Now here we go, Little Brother," Mama Luka said one day.

"There are many a-thousand Jahdu stories," she told Lee Edward. "I know about two hundred of them. I've told you a roomful of Jahdu stories. So that leaves one more roomful of Jahdu stories to tell. Now, you pick out of the air in this room one more Jahdu story."

Lee Edward looked around the room. At last he pointed to an empty space just above Mama Luka's head.

"That one," Lee Edward said.

Mama Luka reached above her head. She cupped her hands around the place Lee Edward had pointed out in the air. And she brought her hands down slowly to her face. Mama Luka opened her mouth and swallowed what had been in her hands.

"Lee Edward, you picked a time-ago story out of the air," she said. "It has a strong taste to it, for it tells how Jahdu found out he had magic power."

"So tell it," Lee Edward said to Mama Luka.

"So I'm getting myself ready," said Mama Luka.

"Lee Edward," began Mama Luka, "the story you picked is about a time not long after Jahdu had been born. He had not much shape then and not much size. And only his face was clear. Jahdu didn't know he had any magic at all.

"Lee Edward, in that time-ago," said Mama Luka, "Jahdu wasn't as tall as you."

"What did his face look like?" asked Lee Edward. He hoped to catch Mama Luka before she had time to think. But Mama Luka wasn't to be caught this day or any other day. No, she wasn't.

"Little Brother, don't you try to trick me," said Mama Luka. "I know better than to talk about the face of Jahdu."

"Just give me a hint," said Lee Edward.

"Child, nobody who has seen the face of Jahdu will tell you what his face looks like. And I have seen it," said Mama Luka, "and I can't tell."

"Well then, get on with the story," said Lee Edward.

"Here it comes," said Mama Luka.

423

THIS IS THE JAHDU STORY WITH A STRONG TASTE THAT MAMA LUKA TOLD TO LEE EDWARD.

Jahdu was running along. He was two feet tall. Yes, he was. And he had been in the world one year.

Jahdu lived high atop the Mountain of Paths. He made his home in the only black gum tupelo tree in the pine forest covering the mountain. From his tree, Jahdu could see all the paths to the valley below. He could see which paths the animal children who lived on the mountain walked along.

Jahdu believed the paths the animal children walked along were good and safe. And only these good and safe paths would Jahdu run along.

But Jahdu was only a year in the world. He did not yet know everything. No, he didn't. One day Jahdu was running along a path behind some animal children. All at once the animal children stopped still.

A bandicoot rat fell to the ground. He grew stiff and he screamed and cried loudly for his mother.

A brown bear cub stood up on one hind leg. He hopped in circles, bumping into a fawn and stepping on a baby otter. The brown bear cub sang a wordless song. The young woodchuck, the raccoon girl, and the wolf child wandered away into the pine wood and were lost. Some of the other animal children sat down on the path, moaning to themselves and trembling all over.

It took Jahdu an hour to gather all of the animal children on the path again. Then he tied a rope around all of them and led them to another path he knew to be good and safe. There, he let them loose.

"I'd better go back to that first path," Jahdu said. "I'd better find out as fast as I can what caused those animal

children to stop still and hop around and fall down and act silly."

Jahdu found the path on which the animal children had stopped still. As he went running down the path, something he couldn't see tried to catch him. But Jahdu was stronger than whatever it was that tried to stop him. He kept right on running along.

"Woogily!" whispered Jahdu to himself. "There are baneberries growing on both sides of this path. Everybody knows baneberries can make animal children sick. I'd better keep on this path to find out what it is that tries to catch me. I'd better find out why baneberries grow on both sides of a good and safe path."

Jahdu stayed on the path. Yes, he did. All at once Jahdu fell into a hole full of thorns.

"Ouch!" said Jahdu. "Thorns have points to hurt Jahdu!" Jahdu jumped out of the hole and bounced into a soft bed of sweet-smelling leaves.

"Woogily!" said Jahdu. "This funny path has good and bad about it. But it surely isn't safe for animal children to walk along."

Jahdu kept right on the good and bad path with baneberries on both sides of it, full of thorn holes and soft beds of sweet-smelling leaves. He ran and he ran until he came to a stream. He sat down in the middle of the stream to cool himself. Suddenly thirteen crawfish started pinching Jahdu. He leaped out of the water.

"Woogily!" said Jahdu. "That's a nice little stream so fresh and cold. But it has thirteen crawfish that can pinch the paws of little animals. I'd better hurry and find out where this funny path ends."

So Jahdu kept on hurrying along the good and bad path with baneberries on both sides, with thorn holes and soft beds of sweet-smelling leaves, and a stream across it with thirteen crawfish.

All at once Jahdu ran smack into a banyan tree at the end of the path. He bounced clear around the banyan tree. Yes, he did. He started running again and ran smack into the banyan tree once more.

"Woogily!" cried Jahdu. "How in the world did a banyan tree get into these pine woods on the Mountain of Paths? Running into banyan trees doesn't feel very good. Little animals will hurt themselves if they go walking into banyan trees!"

Up in the banyan tree was an animal who had a round, sweet face and a bell on its head. And up in the banyan tree was another animal who had a square, mean face and no bell anywhere. Both animals lay side by side peering down at Jahdu.

"I've never seen animals such as you," said Jahdu. "What in the world are you called?"

The animal with a bell on its head spoke first to Jahdu. "I'm called Sweetdream," it said in a soft, sweet voice.

"And I'm Nightmare," said the other animal in a harsh, mean voice. "You're Jahdu and we don't like you."

"Oh, for goodness sake!" said Jahdu. "Like me or not, I'm here to stay. And please tell me why there's a banyan tree at the end of a path on which little animals might walk."

"Because it's here," said Nightmare in a mean voice, "just as Sweetdream and I are here and the path is here, so there!"

"When the bell on my head tinkles," said Sweetdream, "Nightmare and I know little animals are walking along our path."

"Then we use our charms to get them," said Nightmare. "It's such fun watching our spells work on them."

"Just how do your spells work on the little animals?" asked Jahdu.

427

"Well," said Sweetdream, "my spell makes the animals stop still, then hop around and sing sweet songs, and do and say whatever sweet things are in their heads when my spell strikes them."

"And my spell makes them grow stiff," said Nightmare. "They fall to the ground and scream and cry. Or they moan and tremble all over and do whatever bad things are in their thoughts when my spell strikes them."

"Little animals ought to be able to walk along and do as they wish," said Jahdu. "I don't think it's right to use spells on them."

"I don't care what you think," said Sweetdream sweetly. "I do as I please."

"There's nothing you can do to stop *me*," said Nightmare, "so you better go on your way."

Jahdu was angry. He ran to the banyan tree and shook it as hard as he could.

"Come down from that banyan tree, you awful things!" Jahdu yelled. "Come down and I'll surely take care of you!"

Jahdu shook and shook the banyan tree until both animals sitting in it turned purple all over.

"Stop it!" said Sweetdream and Nightmare. "You're making us dizzy and sick!"

"Then come down," said Jahdu, "so Jahdu can take care of you."

"We can't come down," said Sweetdream. "We're attached to this banyan, we can't ever come down!"

Then Jahdu saw that the two animals were growing like figs on the banyan's branches.

"Woogily!" he said. "Now Jahdu's caught you for sure!"

Jahdu ran around and around the banyan tree as fast as he could. He was showing off for the two tree-grown animals.

Yes, he was. And he ran so fast he shook the dust right out of himself.

Jahdu's dust rose up into the banyan tree. It settled on Sweetdream and Nightmare and they fell fast asleep.

Jahdu stopped running.

"Woogily!" he said. "Did I do that? Did my dust put Sweetdream and Nightmare to sleep?"

Wherever the Jahdu dust fell, it put things to sleep. A spider walking along the banyan tree trunk got Jahdu dust on him and fell asleep. A bluebird flying low near the banyan tree got a whiff of the Jahdu dust and had to land in the tree. As the Jahdu dust settled on the bluebird, it fell asleep.

"Woogily!" said Jahdu. "I've got me some magic! I can put things to sleep! Maybe I have more magic. Let me see."

Jahdu tried wishing there was no good and bad path, no Sweetdream and Nightmare and no banyan tree. But this didn't work. No, it didn't. For the path stayed. So did the banyan tree and the sleeping Sweetdream and Nightmare.

Jahdu had another idea. He started running around the banyan tree. Jahdu ran slower and slower and ever so slowly.

The Jahdu dust rose off the two animals up the banyan tree. It rose off the tree trunk and the spider, off the bluebird and off everything. Then the Jahdu dust fell back into Jahdu. All that had been asleep woke up. Sweetdream and Nightmare yawned and stared down at Jahdu.

"Woogily!" said Jahdu. "I can wake things up. I've got me another magic!"

"You shouldn't have put us to sleep," said Sweetdream. "We have to work in the daytime so we can watch the fun."

"You won't watch the fun anymore," said Jahdu, "for I'm going to make you work at night."

"You can't make us do anything we don't want to do," said Nightmare.

"If you don't do what I want you to do, I'll put you to sleep for a week," Jahdu told Nightmare.

"Oh, no," said Sweetdream. "Please don't put him to sleep for a week."

"A month," said Jahdu, feeling good all over.

"All right, you have us," said Nightmare. "Just don't get carried away."

430

Jahdu drew himself up two feet tall. Yes, he did. And he told Sweetdream and Nightmare what he was going to make them do.

"Nightmare will sleep from daylight to nightfall," said Jahdu. "He will work his spell only at night and only on sleeping animals. And if I ever catch him playing around with his spell when it's daylight, I'll put him to sleep for a year!"

Nightmare looked glum but he didn't say a word. He still felt sick from Jahdu's shaking the banyan tree.

"As for Sweetdream," said Jahdu, "she'll work her spell in the daytime only on those little animals who sleep by day. And then only once in a very long while. The rest of her work she will do at night and on sleeping animals, just the same as Nightmare."

Sweetdream smiled sweetly but said nothing.

"I'll never have any fun again watching my spell work," muttered Nightmare.

"That's the truth," said Jahdu. "I'm getting rid of that awful path, too. I'll put it to sleep for the rest of time!"

And so Jahdu did. He ran up and down the path as fast as he could go. Jahdu dust rose from Jahdu and fell all over the path. At once the path was fast asleep. The baneberries on both sides of the path dried up and slept, too. All kinds of forest plants started growing over the path.

Jahdu stood where once the path had begun. Now, young pine saplings started growing there. Jahdu shouted down the path at Sweetdream and Nightmare.

"Your path is gone," Jahdu shouted. "No little animals will come along here! Now you'll have to send your charms out on the night air. Your spells will never again be very strong. For the night air is so light it can carry only a little of your charms at a time!"

Jahdu went running along. Yes, he did. He could run very fast and he could run very slow. He could shake Jahdu dust out of himself and cause it to fall back into himself again. With his magic he could wake things up and put things to sleep.

THIS IS THE END OF THE JAHDU STORY WITH A STRONG TASTE THAT MAMA LUKA TOLD TO LEE EDWARD.